TIMES *crossword* 2

The Best General Crossword in the World

BOOK 2

**Edited and introduced by
Richard Browne**

D0375999

TIMES BOOKS

This edition published 2010
First published in 2001 by Times Books as
The Times 2 Crossword Book 2

HarperCollins*Publishers*
77–85 Fulham Palace Road
Hammersmith
London W6 8JB

www.collins.co.uk

© Times Newspapers Limited 2001

Reprint 1

The Times is a registered trademark of
Times Newspapers Ltd

ISBN 9780007885756

A catalogue record for this book is available from the
British Library.

Typeset in Great Britain by
Davidson Pre-Press Graphics Ltd, Glasgow G3

Printed and bound in Great Britain by
Clays Ltd, Suffolk

Mixed Sources
Product group from well-managed
forests and other controlled sources
www.fsc.org Cert no. SW-COC-001806
© 1996 Forest Stewardship Council

FSC is a non-profit international organisation established to
promote the responsible management of the world's forests.
Products carrying the FSC label are independently certified
to assure consumers that they come from forests that are
managed to meet the social, economic and ecological needs
of present and future generations.

Find out more about HarperCollins and the environment at
www.harpercollins.co.uk/green

INTRODUCTION

Kings, battles, capitals, rivers ... all out of fashion in schools, I am told. These puzzles, then, are for the differently-educated. Or are they? The young audience for the cult radio show *I'm Sorry I haven't a Clue* seems to have no trouble recognising, and laughing hilariously at, the Biblical and historical puns and allusions in the show, which suggests a gratifying familiarity with at least some basic elements of our common national and cultural heritage. Just as well, since I would be baffled trying to compile a crossword that expected solvers to have a background just in project work and key skills.

The puzzles in this selection, then, contain the usual *Times 2* mixture of definitions and general knowledge, and all appeared in *The Times* during the first months of 1998. All except one, that is: puzzle no. 58 appears here for the first time, having been accidentally omitted when the Bank Holiday Jumbo of the day displaced it from its regular back page position, and it failed to land elsewhere. (Its solution, however, duly appeared the following Monday.)

All the answers, if needed, are at the back; as usual with these puzzles, you may find a little extra amusement in noticing additional themes or patterns in the completed grids of some of them. Some are fairly obvious; others less so. Enjoy!

Richard Browne
Times 2 Editor

THE PUZZLES

ACROSS

1 Mouth cosmetic (8)

7 Previous; a religious (5)

8 A butterfly; sulphur (once) (9)

9 Meadow (3)

10 Went; socialist (4)

11 Boy's name; was wicked (*reversed*) (6)

13 SI temperature unit (6)

14 Renter of property (6)

17 Ceramic worker; vaguely fill time (6)

18 Comfily ensconced (4)

20 Hatchet (3)

22 Investigator (9)

23 Varlet; jack (5)

24 (Girl) receiving patronage (8)

DOWN

1 Defamatory publication (5)

2 Agonising (7)

3 Assigned job (4)

4 Anger; sounds like *part of jacket* (6)

5 Housman's were *blue-remembered* (5)

6 Syrup; cloying flattery (7)

7 Small coins (7)

12 Turbulent current (7)

13 In pub, 15 to tape (7)

15 Art of the voice (7)

16 Trusted (older) adviser (6)

17 Part of flower; "now sleeps the crimson —" (*Tennyson*) (5)

19 Incumbent's plot of land (5)

21 North Briton (4)

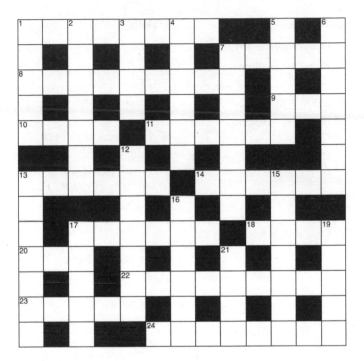

ACROSS

1 Frank, honest (6)

5 Piecing-together puzzle (6)

8 Door-frame side (4)

9 Horse-equipment business (8)

10 Climbing-plant frame (7)

11 Insipid (5)

13 Disturb (settled situation) (4,3,4)

16 Chuck; supporting strap (5)

18 Dim; puzzling (7)

21 Wrist ornament (8)

22 Useless; conceited (4)

23 Charlie —, *Lord Jim* narrator (*Conrad*) (6)

24 Jacob —, Scrooge's partner (*Dickens*) (6)

DOWN

2 Non-professional (7)

3 Fix (computer program) (5)

4 Uninhabited; friendless (8)

5 New Testament epistle; — the 18, *Hardy* (4)

6 Italian astronomer, Inquisition victim (7)

7 Brother of Moses (5)

12 Word for word (8)

14 Sneering; suspecting worst motives (7)

15 Coarse pâté (7)

17 Immature insect form (5)

19 Protect; deal with (5)

20 Bird's nail (4)

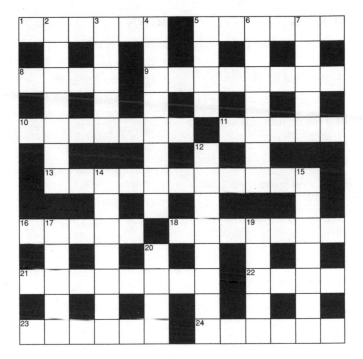

ACROSS

3 Enormous bird (*Sinbad*) (3)

8 Jewelled headdress (5)

9 Stir up, make anxious (7)

10 Loss of wits (7)

11 Increased (5)

12 Capital of Germany (6)

14 Lowest parts (of e.g. sea) (6)

15 Cite (as example) (6)

17 Parentless child (6)

20 Jeans cloth (5)

21 Got thinner towards end (7)

24 Academic class (7)

25 Forearm joint (5)

26 Act as crew of (3)

DOWN

1 Restrain; word root (4)

2 Be indulgent, accommodating (to weakness) (6)

3 Speed contest; rapid current (4)

4 Motive; lawsuit (5)

5 Shakespearian tragedy (4,4)

6 Go to restaurant; etch (3,3)

7 *Idylls of the King* poet (8)

12 Wave threateningly (8)

13 Arriving; new (e.g. government) (8)

16 Generator; energetic person (6)

18 Helena's rival (*MND*) (6)

19 Tempest (5)

22 Chessman; dupe (4)

23 Responsibility; tax (4)

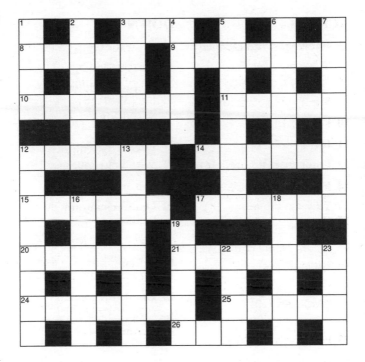

ACROSS

1 Put into other words (10)

8 Staying power (7)

9 Freight boat; shove (in) (5)

10 Cooker (4)

11 More powerful (8)

13 Utter snarl-up (6)

15 Start (fire) (6)

17 Tiny sea organisms (8)

18 Oh dear! (4)

21 Wagner *Ring* river (5)

22 Rumour (7)

23 Fine writing; sales brochures (10)

DOWN

2 Astound (5)

3 Surrounded by (4)

4 Warm, friendly; big (meal) (6)

5 Food of the gods (8)

6 Made very angry (7)

7 With bold courage (10)

8 Wet blanket (10)

12 Unfair charge by landlord (4-4)

14 Icy (7)

16 Ritually eatable (*Jewish*) (6)

19 CD-reading beam (5)

20 Excrescence, may be charmed away (4)

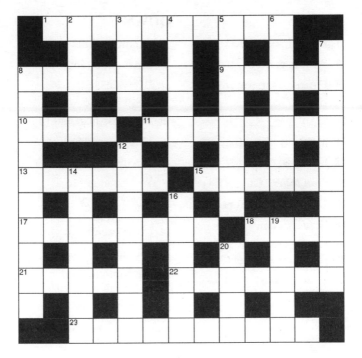

ACROSS

1 Uneasy feeling (7)

5 At this place (4)

8 Officer's servant (6)

9 Prolong (6)

10 An order to attend court (8)

12 Secluded corner (4)

13 *Gondoliers* Duke (5,4)

17 Dismiss; enthuse (4)

18 France/Spain mountains (8)

20 Regular earnings (6)

21 Evening-dress neckwear (3,3)

23 (Tree) trunk (4)

24 Raging 17 (7)

DOWN

2 Counting frame (6)

3 Purpose; direct (at target) (3)

4 Burn slightly (5)

5 Non-stop accident (3-3-3)

6 Haphazard (6)

7 Occupant of premises (6)

11 Proceeds of petty theft (9)

14 Light breeze (6)

15 Violent woman (6)

16 Well-intentioned; unthreatening (6)

19 Cock bird, killed by Sparrow (5)

22 Misery (3)

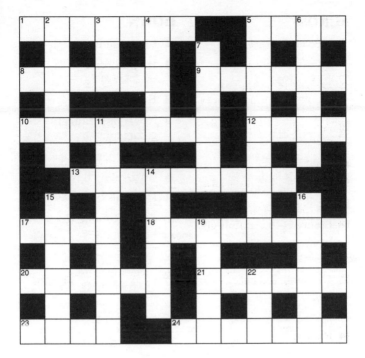

ACROSS

6 Account dishonestly (4,3,5)

7 Ill will (6)

8 Number of fluid ounces in pint (6)

9 Spring; fit (4)

10 Laughably small (8)

12 Britain's highest mountain (3,5)

16 Charge per unit; to deserve (4)

18 A streaming in (of crowd) (6)

20 Unparalleled (6)

21 Progress of material success (4,2,6)

DOWN

1 Plain broth (8)

2 Be present at; wait upon (6)

3 Drink of the gods (6)

4 Observe; scribbled comment (4)

5 One moving on ice (6)

6 Bird; lifting device (5)

11 Unbending; honest (8)

13 Group of nine (6)

14 Street interview (3,3)

15 Artist's workroom (6)

17 Fasten; tomato cluster (5)

19 Be deprived of (4)

ACROSS

1 Husks; banter (5)

4 With unfounded hope (7)

8 Failure to follow correct line (9)

9 Wave; a wit (3)

10 Hurry; a cricket score (3)

11 See (9)

12 (Played) without a score (2,3)

13 Be evasive; (engine) cut out (5)

16 Really enjoy oneself (4,1,4)

18 A share; slight wound (3)

20 Song; appearance (3)

21 Month of Robespierre's fall (9)

22 When Solomon Grundy was christened (7)

23 Welsh town; below (5)

DOWN

1 A pine, sweet-smelling wood (5)

2 Progress; lend (7)

3 Bowled over (13)

4 Caprice; fanciful humour (6)

5 Bible love-poem book (4,2,7)

6 Not so many (5)

7 Rational (7)

12 (Recited) without book (2,5)

14 Rural paradise (7)

15 Up till just now (6)

17 Section of e.g. hymn (5)

19 Portable light (5)

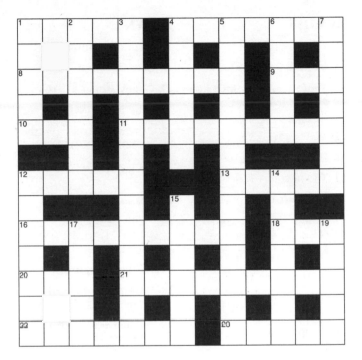

ACROSS

5 Ill-advised (6)

7 Irrational fear (6)

9 Shore region; sounds like *prosaic* (8)

11 Look for (4)

12 Gift voucher; nominal (5)

13 The next day (*poet.*) (6)

15 Misery (6)

17 Defend; it had *Yeomen* (*G. & S.*) (5)

19 Garden water pipe (4)

20 Of the throat (8)

22 River, proverbially *Blue* (6)

23 Pamper (6)

DOWN

1 Item of ammo (6)

2 Scorch, brand (4)

3 Greek sun god ... (6)

4 ... lie in his rays (4)

6 (The same to you) only more so (4,5,2)

8 Capital of Argentina (6,5)

10 Possessor (5)

14 "All's — with the world!" (*Pippa Passes*) (5)

16 Wild parties (6)

18 Remove (from sequence) (6)

19 Animal skin; with 11, a game (4)

21 Horse equipment; a sailing course (4)

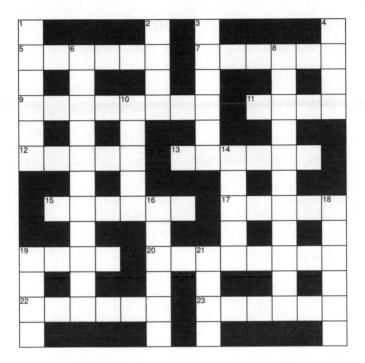

ACROSS

1 Bogus doctor (5)

4 Drum; embroidery frame (7)

8 Water-ski board; (driver) lose control in wet (9)

9 (Tide) recede (3)

10 State of pique; blow hard (4)

11 Paraffin oil (8)

13 Of the flesh (6)

14 (E.g. face) spotty (6)

17 An emperor; a pig (*Orwell*) (8)

19 Responsibility (4)

22 Mother of Cain (3)

23 Hustling for success (2,3,4)

24 Football teams (7)

25 Utterly untypical (5)

DOWN

1 Annul (verdict) (5)

2 Rock as water source (7)

3 French military cap (4)

4 England's longest river (6)

5 Memory aid (8)

6 Grossly fat (5)

7 Elastic; toughly flexible (7)

12 Poetry muse; a steam organ (8)

13 Call (meeting) (7)

15 Emergency (landing); a byword for flatness (7)

16 Spanish Assembly; a Conquistador (6)

18 Irritate (5)

20 (E.g. dust) particle (5)

21 Hard of hearing (4)

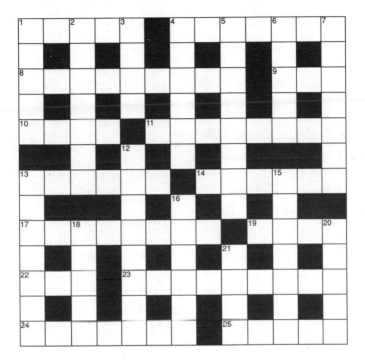

ACROSS

1 Avoid; military command (4)

3 Shameless (wrongdoing) (8)

8 True statement (4)

9 One from Kingston (8)

11 Obscenely defamatory (10)

14 Astute insight (6)

15 Foil, butt (6)

17 Barred liftable gate (10)

20 Fragrant (plant) (8)

21 Pottery oven (4)

22 *Ode to Joy* poet (8)

23 Curtain (4)

DOWN

1 Large-majority constituency (4,4)

2 Oily, ingratiating (8)

4 Answerable (6)

5 Unprovoked (10)

6 Expert (4-); roguish (4)

7 Sound quality; musical interval (4)

10 General mêlée (4-3-3)

12 Hot compress (8)

13 Occurring at certain times of year (8)

16 Conflict; *none worth* Landor's (6)

18 Bulk; a service (4)

19 Scottish lake, sea arm (4)

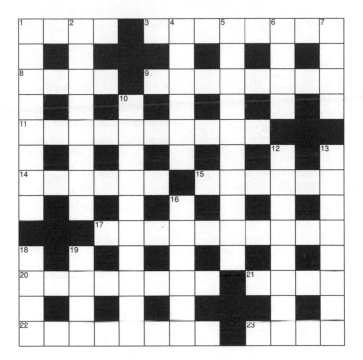

ACROSS

1 Sell (*slang*); thrash (4)

4 Intimidate (8)

8 Send, pass on (8)

9 Spout out (4)

10 Improvised (2,3)

11 Diocese of Rome (4,3)

13 Glossy coating, especially of teeth (6)

15 A dog; creator of exam (6)

18 When Heaven lies about us (*Wordsworth*) (7)

20 Cheerful; a marine (*slang*) (5)

23 Garden pest; pellet (4)

24 Sea pollution trail (3,5)

25 Old fire-retardant (8)

26 Window frame; cloth strip (4)

DOWN

2 Vivid, shocking (5)

3 Enticed (7)

4 Collide with; a swelling (4)

5 A building in yard (8)

6 Pushchair; infested (5)

7 Spartan (7)

10 Tailless primate (3)

12 Faint; sudden darkness (8)

14 Take aback; negation of 22? (7)

16 Lover of Cressida (7)

17 Light-beam (3)

19 Develop point of view (5)

21 Place (*legal*); set of points (*maths*) (5)

22 In addition (4)

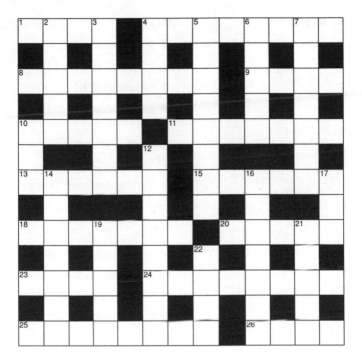

ACROSS

1 Elder and Younger PMs (4)

3 Driving force (7)

8 Caustically sharp (wit) (7)

9 Tripoli its capital (5)

10 Secret hoard (5)

11 Type of victory, as costly as defeat (7)

13 Link; colleague (9)

17 Short piece from e.g. book (7)

19 More private, secret (5)

20 Move mazily, as smoke (5)

22 Nicotine plant (7)

23 Riled (7)

24 Apollo's instrument (4)

DOWN

1 Fish; sounds like *site* (6)

2 Forceful, incisive (9)

3 Disabled (13)

4 Of the northernmost regions (5)

5 Bath; slow boat (3)

6 Small cloth sample (6)

7 Haunt; dominate mind of (6)

12 Commotion (after absconder) (3,3,3)

14 With hands on hips (6)

15 Japanese hostess (6)

16 Guiding channel (6)

18 Calm (suspicion) (5)

21 Atom with extra/missing electron (3)

ACROSS

1 Letters; people in play (10)

8 Feat; make use of (7)

9 Force (on one) (5)

10 Cooperative group (4)

11 Big eater (8)

13 Curl lip (5)

14 Passion; bright orange/red (5)

16 Radio user; old BBC magazine (8)

17 Water creature; strengthening plate (4)

20 Cheated; hurt by wasp (5)

21 Niceties, to be minded (2,3,2)

22 El Alamein victor (10)

DOWN

1 Storage box (5)

2 First course with letters in (8,4)

3 Unit of matter (4); first half of alphabet? (1,2,1)

4 Indelible skin decoration (6)

5 The rabble (4-4)

6 Bursting with health (3,2,1,6)

7 Heavy pudding (6)

12 Broken chord (8)

13 Publicity display; a little soda water (6)

15 Tyrant (6)

18 A dog; hoarse (5)

19 Ring of light (4)

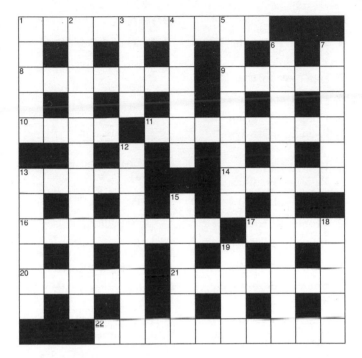

ACROSS

1 Scottish oatmeal cake (7)

5 Feel passion; char (4)

9 French workman's cap (5)

10 Italian port, two post-World War 1 treaties (7)

11 Trained for man's use, for home life (12)

12 Thrown plate (6)

13 (Gone) off course (6)

16 Adverse, ominous (12)

19 On the other hand (7)

20 Sort of whiskey, bull, stew (5)

21 John, Beau, Ogden — (4)

22 Later this evening (7)

DOWN

1 Newborn, tiny (4)

2 Apprehensive (7)

3 Alert, watchful (2,3,3,4)

4 Unarmed combat (Japan) (6)

6 Not illuminated (5)

7 Twelve; highest (sun) (4-3)

8 Astronauts' base (5,7)

12 French king's eldest son (7)

14 Rich (*slang*); group of Stones (7)

15 Tower in e.g. castle wall (6)

17 Young deer; is obsequious (5)

18 Tiniest amount; a Sunday (4)

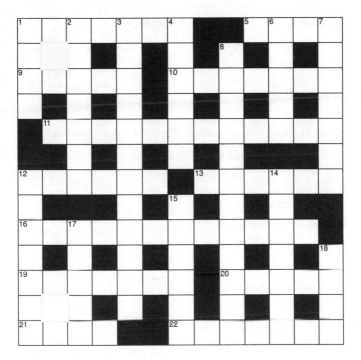

ACROSS

7 Tibetan priest (4)

8 Will administrator (8)

9 Greater (6)

10 Henry —, author; tradesman (e.g. of Dee) (6)

11 Body of water; red dye (4)

12 A shrub; *red alone* (*anagram*) (8)

15 Unwanted remnants (8)

17 Head covering (4)

18 Disreputable, shifty (6)

21 Wise old Greek (*Iliad*) (6)

22 One hanging about idly (8)

23 Scowl, be menacing (4)

DOWN

1 Computer info store (8)

2 Hang; hold out enticingly (6)

3 End-of-affair (letter) (4,4)

4 Consider, judge (4)

5 Irish capital (6)

6 Lavish foolish love (on) (4)

13 Setting of *Hamlet* (8)

14 Closedown programme (8)

16 Abandon occupancy of (6)

17 Shove; be aggressive salesman (6)

19 Instrument, has *d'amore* version (4)

20 Charlotte Brontë's Jane (4)

ACROSS

1 Small; Dickens's *Dorrit* (6)
4 Roman emperor title (6)
9 Top-people guide (4,3)
10 Milk can; butter-maker (5)
11 Profit; give in (5)
13 Cautious, attentive (7)
14 Second person pronoun (3)
15 Soiled (5)
16 Rodent; Pied Piper victim (3)
17 River 4 crucially crossed (7)
19 Impatient, keen (5)
21 Take as one's own (5)
22 Egg white (7)
24 Talk under one's breath (6)
25 James —, US gangster-film actor (6)

DOWN

1 L. S. —, industrial painter (5)
2 Henry —, US *Walden* author (7)
3 Moo (3)
5 Original model; unconscious image (*Jung*) (9)
6 Extinguish; some tobacco (5)
7 Curl of hair (7)
8 Partner's parent; her tongue a plant (6-2-3)
12 To whom e.g. book is inscribed (9)
14 Can drink, when sun over it (*nautical*) (4-3)
16 Course of diet (7)
18 Encourage, lift (5)
20 Long-, loose-limbed (5)
23 Snake; feather scarf (3)

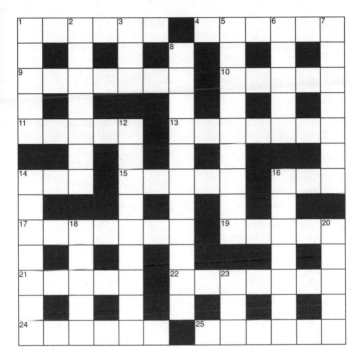

ACROSS

1 Deceptive lightening (5,4)

6 Tiny taste from glass (3)

8 Workforce; surveying rod (5)

9 Rostrum; popular leader (7)

10 Stolid calmness (6)

12 Pivot joint; (philatelic) mount (5)

13 Grow strongly; prosper (6)

14 Forcibly persuade (6)

17 (Ear) anvil bone (5)

19 Staunch; take into custody (6)

21 Roman soldiers' god (7)

22 10% tax (5)

23 Tear (3); farewell (1,1,1)

24 Unexciting chef (5,4)

DOWN

1 Quick; unable to move (4)

2 Tanned skin (7)

3 Mischievous spirit (3)

4 Breathing disorder (6)

5 Man next door (9)

6 Reject with contempt (5)

7 Go before (7)

11 Listen at window (9)

13 Cutter; a Vicar of Bray (7)

15 Rice/stock dish (7)

16 Sickness; revulsion (6)

18 Dissected; upset (3,2)

20 Gesture (*poetic*); mountain stream (4)

22 Can; element Sn (3)

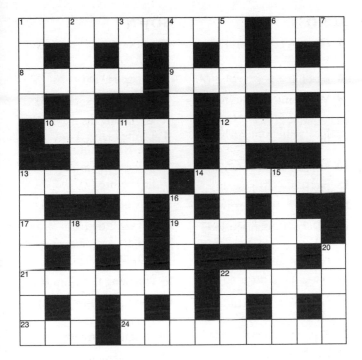

ACROSS

7 (Horse) coat sprinkled with white (4)

8 Fit of anger; a stroke (8)

9 Vague, misty state (8)

10 Summit (4)

11 Peeping Tom (6)

13 Start golf round (3,3)

15 Horrified (6)

17 Require; state firmly (6)

19 Photo; guess; injection (4)

21 All-embracing (8)

23 Hat maker (8)

24 Uninteresting (colour) (4)

DOWN

1 (Going) very cheaply (3,1,4)

2 Complete (6)

3 Bringer of destruction (4)

4 Dante Gabriel —, Pre-Raphaelite (8)

5 Missing quantity of liquid (6)

6 Wheelshaft (4)

12 Saying little (8)

14 Celebration; Britain's, in 1951 (8)

16 Hun king (6)

18 Poor quality (material) (6)

20 Greeting; bad weather (4)

22 Go off; change colour; reach (an age) (4)

ACROSS

7 An eccentric; starting handle (5)

8 Fish; *a few lie* about (7)

9 Outstanding performance (7)

10 Bird; Irish dean, satirist (5)

11 Assistance (4)

12 Pocket cutter (8)

15 Catastrophe (8)

16 Mark; place; observe (4)

19 Shaver (5)

21 Ralph Waldo —, US poet (7)

22 Seek, request earnestly (7)

23 Uttered; part of wheel (5)

DOWN

1 Frustrate; sort of egg, fir, mist (6)

2 Rod-shaped pathogen (8)

3 Do (task) carelessly fast (5)

4 Japanese ivory toggle (7)

5 Flightless bird; a fruit (4)

6 Insect; Stalky's friend (*Kipling*) (6)

8 Success in task; an escutcheon (11)

13 False person; 9 and 15 *ac*, for Kipling (8)

14 Flightless bird; one refusing to face facts (7)

15 Compulsion (6)

17 Offer; sore (6)

18 — Owens, James; David's father (5)

20 Emile —, wrote *J'accuse* (4)

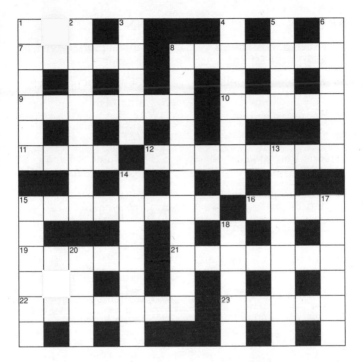

ACROSS

1 Timer, has two notes (6,5)

8 An accent; four-minim note (5)

9 Nauseous; irritable (7)

10 Lie in wait (4)

11 New European republic, 1993 (8)

13 Pierre Auguste —, Impressionist (6)

14 A seeming automaton (6)

17 Outdoor cooked meal (8)

19 Feudal land (4)

22 Easily broken (7)

23 Bestow (5)

24 Fantasy, pretence (4-7)

DOWN

1 Political plotters' group (5)

2 NCO's stripe shape (7)

3 Cattle (4)

4 Make shoes; a road stone (6)

5 Forgetfulness; Time's *alms for* it (*Troilus*) (8)

6 Sales booth (5)

7 Run away (6)

12 Companion, helper (8)

13 Snub (6)

15 Group of battalions (7)

16 Excellent, grand (6)

18 Sphere, kingdom (5)

20 Evade, misrepresent (issue); a sweet (5)

21 Become boring; shroud (4)

ACROSS

1 Speed, urgency (5)

4 Partner; use thriftily (7)

8 Spanish treasure ship (7)

9 Sydney beach (5)

10 Pier, dock (5)

11 Protection; scutcheon (6)

13 A Gorgon; a jellyfish (6)

15 Las Vegas state (6)

18 Regular, even (6)

20 Aver; condition (5)

22 Tawny nestling (5)

23 Chemical element variant (7)

24 To merit (7)

25 Card-game rule-book compiler (5)

DOWN

1 Athletics event; the naughty for it (4,4)

2 Acknowledged officer (7)

3 Foe (5)

4 Frank, trustworthy (6)

5 (Flood, tumult) go down (7)

6 Make void (5)

7 Irish assembly (4)

12 Unaided vision (5,3)

14 Disperse (7)

16 Comparison drawing similarity (7)

17 Journalist's name on column (2-4)

19 Stories; emergency jury (5)

20 A sin; an animal (5)

21 Precious metal (4)

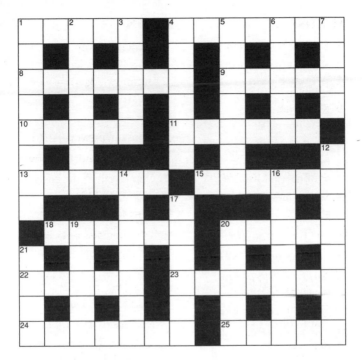

ACROSS

1 Dispatch; sudden bang (6)

4 A French pastry (6)

8 Destiny (4)

9 Become cordial with (8)

10 Food shopping (9)

13 Dumas musketeer; a monastic Mount (5)

15 Incantation; work period (5)

16 Fop (5)

18 Magnifying tube (9)

21 Appreciation of one deceased (8)

22 Side of pitch; wound (game bird) (4)

23 Prize; victory memorial (6)

24 Formidable adversary; deposit on teeth (6)

DOWN

1 Place of safety (6)

2 Disease-causing organism (8)

3 Dahlia root; potato stem (5)

5 Encased pupa (9)

6 Yemen port (4)

7 Centre/circumference line (6)

11 One receptive to beggar (4,5)

12 Model of perfection (5)

14 One living for pleasure (8)

16 Godly, prayerful (6)

17 Radioactivity counter inventor (6)

19 Country Exodus was out of (5)

20 Open-air pool (4)

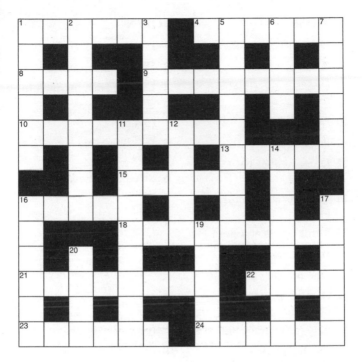

ACROSS

4 Driver's compartment (3)

8 A wrench (7)

9 Coordinate; straighten (5)

10 Bonus; more (5)

11 Poise (7)

12 Decisive gunfight (5-3); suddenly extend (5,3)

14 English saint, historian (4)

15 Verdi Egyptian opera (4)

16 Weight, intensity (8)

20 One messing up task (7)

21 Darling girl (*Peter Pan*) (5)

23 Play (instrument) idly (5)

24 Tomb inscription (7)

25 Block (action; of soap) (3)

DOWN

1 Evaluate (6)

2 With dull surface (4)

3 Unopened, unharmed (6)

4 Scream in alarm (*slang*) (3,4,6)

5 Snooker-table line, area (5)

6 Swedish botanist, naming-system inventor (8)

7 In celebratory mode (2,4)

13 Humdrum; unvarying parts of Mass (8)

15 Head nun (6)

17 US non-mainland state (6)

18 Mower's implement (6)

19 Ascend (5)

22 Trim; undiluted (4)

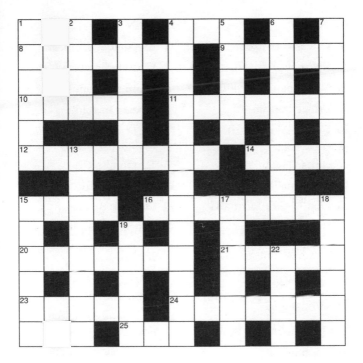

ACROSS

3 One still alive (8)

7 Place of pilgrimage (6)

8 Village; a play (6)

9 Projecting rim (6)

10 Compassionate (6)

11 Part of leg, sounds like *cure* (4)

13 Show malicious glee (5)

15 First wife of Jacob (4)

17 Belittle (6)

18 (Small) share (6)

19 Glory; ten or higher (*bridge*) (6)

20 Cup rest (6)

21 Fraught with danger (8)

DOWN

1 Slope gently; put off (6)

2 Gesture; important (6)

3 More than one (7)

4 Road, rail bridge (7)

5 French satirist, *Candide* author (8)

6 Economise (8)

11 Poverty, distress (8)

12 One setting test (8)

13 Slow and steady (7)

14 Attend to; where one lives (7)

15 (Chemical) test, paper (6)

16 Portuguese Atlantic islands (6)

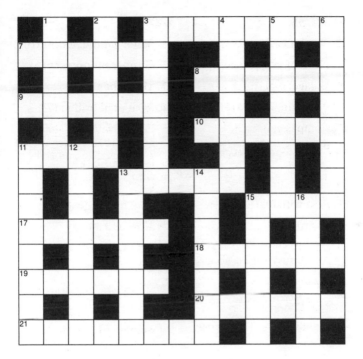

ACROSS

1 Work fast, carelessly (3,7)

7 Menial; liveried servant (7)

8 Firm, hard (5)

10 Result (7)

11 Horseman; addendum (5)

12 Herald's jacket (6)

15 Toboggan (6)

17 Supply with kit (5)

18 Prepare to fence! (2,5)

21 Move furtively, crabwise (5)

22 St. Thomas —, theologian (7)

23 De Gaulle's group, 1940 (4,6)

DOWN

1 Woo; royal household (5)

2 Capital of Japan (5)

3 Element O (6)

4 Non-artificial; uncultivated (state) (7)

5 (Cape) passed; (number) with fraction ignored (7)

6 Simple; without exertion (10)

9 Practical intelligence (5,5)

13 Bad mistake (7)

14 Full (of food) (7)

16 Mend; go (to) (6)

19 Quark-joining particle (5)

20 (US) cattle farm (5)

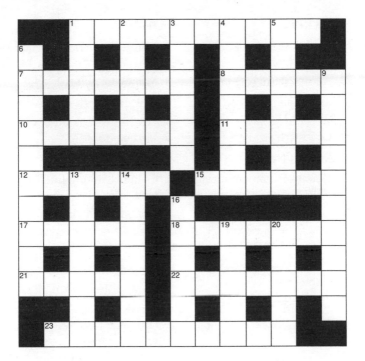

ACROSS

1 Bumpy skin from cold, fright (5-5)

9 Accept share (of) (7)

10 Sharp, pungent (e.g. smell) (5)

11 Loud (crowd) noise (4)

12 Lay out (cash) (8)

14 Georg —, mathematician; church singer (6)

15 Unimportant facts (6)

18 Of sound; unamplified (guitar) (8)

20 — of Cleves, of Green Gables (4)

22 Gandhi's country (5)

23 On horseback; went up (7)

24 Hopeless idea; one scratching (3-7)

DOWN

2 Ellipse; a cricket ground (4)

3 Money in coin (6)

4 Gustave —, *Bovary* author (8)

5 Mistake (5)

6 Ulterior motive (6,6)

7 Gain (of value); thanks (12)

8 Command; make priest (6)

13 Unvarying, faithful (8)

16 Conceit; a case, a Fair (6)

17 Cook gently; be about to rage (6)

19 (In) ancient (days) (*archaic*) (5)

21 Lovably sweet (4)

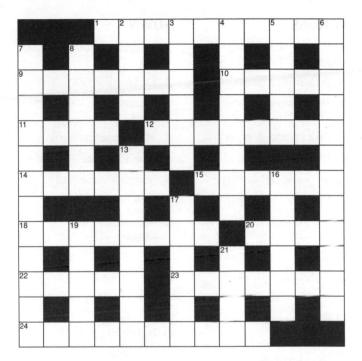

ACROSS

1 Brightly coloured; graphic (5)

4 Atone for (7)

8 Inheritance, endowment (9)

9 Fish eggs; a deer (3)

10 Black; secret (4)

11 Showing elation (8)

13 Flinched (with pain) (6)

14 (E.g. quiz contestant's) signalling device (6)

17 Gilbert's partner (8)

19 Pollution haze (4)

22 Jack Sprat's wife ate it (3)

23 Craven behaviour (9)

24 Portable light (7)

25 Lost force, declined (5)

DOWN

1 Insipid; lacking content (5)

2 Old soldier (7)

3 Leak slowly; 1 *dn* person (4)

4 Mass departure (6)

5 Size, shape of body (8)

6 Main blood-vessel (5)

7 Voter; Hanover ruler (7)

12 Disappointingly average (8)

13 Pensive, sad (7)

15 One from Lusaka (7)

16 *Origin of Species* author (6)

18 Blurt out; pretend (3,2)

20 Excess appetite (5)

21 Front of vessel (4)

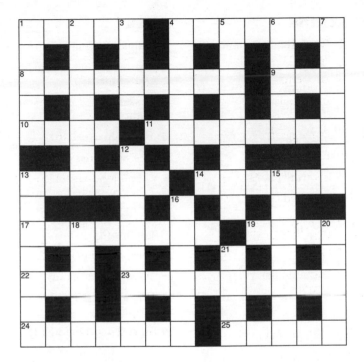

ACROSS

2 More likely than not (8)

6 African expedition (6)

8 Hurtling; going by air (6)

9 Specially made (suit) (7)

10 Thieves' slang (5)

12 Rashness (10)

16 Neck and neck (*especially US*) (3,3,4)

18 Leaves; even (5)

20 Escape; go on holiday (3,4)

21 Attack, criticise, violently (6)

22 Older, more important (6)

23 Fine weather (8)

DOWN

1 Capital of Sicily (7)

2 Taken into hand; gained (speed) (6,2)

3 *Comédie humaine* author (6)

4 Fetch (5)

5 The last Kings Henry, Edward (6)

7 Obvious; type of heir (8)

11 Hold back (8)

13 Gibberish (8)

14 Eight-sided figure (7)

15 Wives of braves (6)

17 Major Old Testament prophet (6)

19 Henrik —, dramatist (5)

ACROSS

1 Old Labourite (9)

6 Rudiments of reading (1,1,1)

8 Spilt; emotionally hurt (5)

9 Tendency to resist motion (7)

10 (Watchman) make rounds (6)

12 A bedtime drink (5)

13 Foul smell (6)

14 Deviously achieve, obtain (6)

17 Leisurely walk (5)

19 Milne's gloomy donkey (6)

21 Idle chatter (7)

22 Greek *th* (5)

23 Teachers union (*abbr.*); one with *bolt* (3)

24 Turned up (nose) (9)

DOWN

1 Speck of soot (4)

2 Waterfall (7)

3 Paintings, etc. (3)

4 Frozen drips (6)

5 Rule by priestly caste (9)

6 Loft room (5)

7 Travesty; parlour-game episode (7)

11 Reader, I (*Jane Eyre*) married him (9)

13 Whet (7)

15 Works outdoors; the salley —, *Yeats* (7)

16 Flaw; go over to enemy (6)

18 Wild animal (5)

20 Green stone; a nag (4)

22 Excessively; also (3)

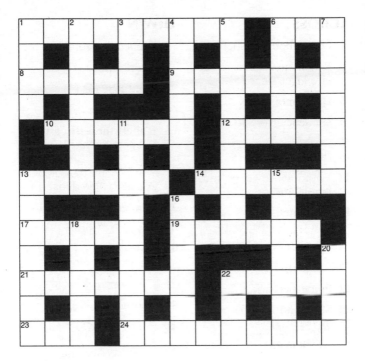

ACROSS

1 Natural environment (7)

5 Footwear; hotel employee once (5)

8 Be king (5)

9 Unvarying; placid (7)

10 Desperately vital (matter) (4-3-5)

12 Withdraw (from political union) (6)

14 Johannes —, laws-of-motion discoverer (6)

17 Disassemble (4,2,6)

21 Short axe (7)

22 Paperwork (5)

23 Stains; notices (5)

24 Type of jacket; Sir Winston — Churchill (7)

DOWN

1 Innocuous (8)

2 Short; advise (5)

3 Beer mug (7)

4 With-it (6)

5 Robert the —: Lenny —, US comedian (5)

6 Electron's path (7)

7 A canal; 1956 debacle (4)

11 One in confinement (8)

13 Division of book (7)

15 Type of Muslim country (7)

16 Developed embryo (6)

18 Characteristic spirit (5)

19 Funny man (5)

20 Feigned (4)

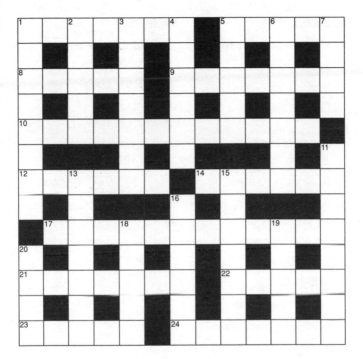

ACROSS

1 Himalayan guide (6)

5 Exasperated sound (4)

8 Boast; a card-game (4)

9 Hostile (8)

10 Less enthusiastic second thoughts (4,4)

11 Pith, argument (4)

12 Bequest (6)

14 Burroughs' Lord of the Jungle (6)

16 US Mormon state (4)

18 Bullfighter (8)

20 Soil, sully (8)

21 Spanish portraitist (4)

22 Slide out of control (4)

23 Negotiation under truce (6)

DOWN

2 Endocrine-gland product (7)

3 Unyielding (5)

4 You're lying! (1,6,5)

5 Dirty laugh (7)

6 It's greener, beyond the hill (5)

7 Absolute rule (12)

13 Mortified (7)

15 Pain-relieving (7)

17 Finely adjust; pinch (e.g. ear) (5)

19 Rage (5)

ACROSS

1 Rather fat (5)
4 Milk/cornflour sauce (7)
8 Wrestled (7)
9 American elk (5)
10 A flower; an instrument (5)
11 Voice-box (6)
13 Itinerant mender (6)
15 A seafood; prise (out) (6)
18 Portuguese port, on Douro (6)
20 Up and active (5)
22 Indian language (5)
23 Able to read minds (7)
24 Scots purse (7)
25 Church assembly (5)

DOWN

1 Smarten oneself up (8)
2 Instrument; Wedding-Guest heard it (*Coleridge*) (7)
3 Crimean town, 1945 conference (5)
4 Nice to hug (6)
5 Japanese warrior caste (7)
6 Oak fruit (5)
7 Piece for two (4)
12 In stepped layers (8)
14 Before (7)
16 Chef's domain (7)
17 Detachable ticket (6)
19 Christmas show (*abbr.*) (5)
20 Bottomless pit (5)
21 In such a way (4)

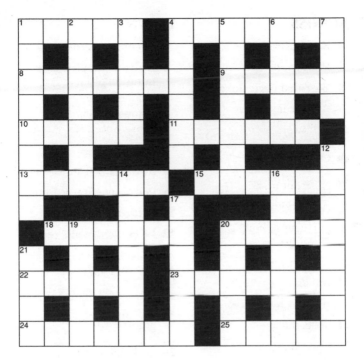

ACROSS

4 Road up to house (5)

7 Roof-reeder (8)

8 Barrie's pirate; boxer's punch (4)

9 Jean Jacques —, *Confessions* author (8)

10 Quick look (6)

13 Desperate food shortage (6)

14 Have for choice (6)

15 Home (*symbol.*); bottom of furnace (6)

18 Most astounding, beautiful (8)

19 Haul; influence (4)

20 Final (8)

21 Use broom; old chimney climber (5)

DOWN

1 Gentle walk (6)

2 Philip —, poet, was Hull librarian (6)

3 Accumulate (e.g. interest) (6)

4 Horse obedience training (8)

5 Lower; worse (8)

6 Pardon; reason (6)

11 Sufficient (8)

12 Mops; scoops the pool (6,2)

14 Fish star-sign (6)

15 Scots offal dish (6)

16 Attraction; request to umpire (6)

17 Bank cashier (6)

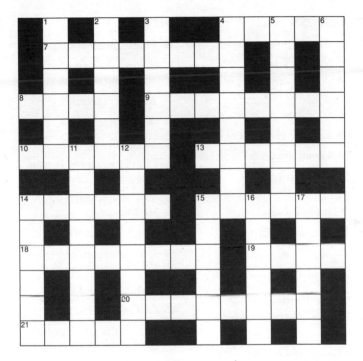

ACROSS

1 Think darkly; set of offspring (5)

4 Tiniest discrete amount; a theory (7)

8 Indefensibly unfair (13)

9 Squinting; awry (8)

10 Limbs; bingo "eleven" (4)

12 Dried grape (6)

13 Alcohol; water (for beer-making) (6)

16 Cousin's mum (4)

17 Not equally balanced (8)

20 Israeli farm commune (7)

21 In the vicinity; a pub (5)

22 Damage beyond repair (5)

23 Ireland such an isle (7)

DOWN

1 Doorman; head-high ball (7)

2 Arousing complaint (13)

3 Reading disorder (8)

4 Arrow holder (6)

5 Greedy (4)

6 Dramatic scene; frozen stage action (7)

7 Satisfies; is introduced to (5)

11 Mix into water (8)

14 Coloured red; unkempt (7)

15 Spout on hose (6)

16 Out of true (5)

18 Russian country cottage (5)

19 Chinese boat; lumber (4)

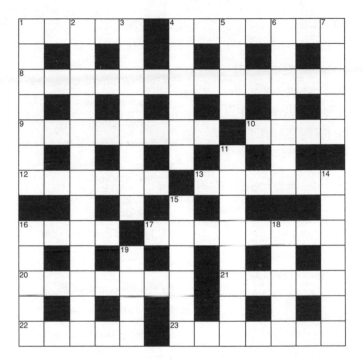

ACROSS

1 Parvenu (7)

5 Gentlewoman (4)

8 Stout stick (6)

9 Non-transparent (6)

10 Henry VI's queen (8)

12 Entry-room; sounds like *pull* (4)

13 Without precedent (7-2)

17 Back of head; counting of votes (4)

18 One supplying (provisions) (8)

20 Hot season (6)

21 Defame, malign (6)

23 Blood vessel; sounds like *conceited* (4)

24 Field where James IV died, 1513 (7)

DOWN

2 More than one (*grammar*) (6)

3 Label; child's game (3)

4 Stationery item; king (5)

5 Hateful (9)

6 Twice as much (6)

7 The Grossmiths' *Nobody* (6)

11 Smugglers; they prefer blondes (9)

14 The sun never set on ours (6)

15 Capacity; a book (6)

16 Cushion as seat (6)

19 Fellow-competitor (5)

22 (Box) top (3)

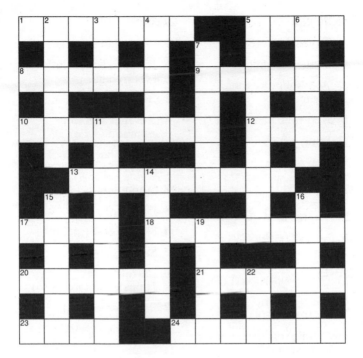

ACROSS

1 Truthfulness (8)

5 Swiss mountains (4)

9 Alcohol-processing organ (5)

10 Return to bad ways (7)

11 Imply (7)

12 Bell-shaped spring flower (5)

13 Interplanetary vehicle (9)

18 Tender, hold out (5)

20 Insult (7)

22 Biassed; attracted (to) (7)

23 Gather (little bits) (5)

24 Hazardous ridge; shorten sail (4)

25 Putting together; a meeting (8)

DOWN

1 Overnight bag (6)

2 Ruinous actions, effects (7)

3 Bendy line (5)

4 Reverse a (losing) situation (4,3,6)

6 Folded-back part of jacket (5)

7 Somnolent (6)

8 Hold tight; part of car (6)

14 Skilful, deft (6)

15 Saw, saying (7)

16 Barrel-maker; James Fenimore — (6)

17 Parsimonious (6)

19 Counterfeit; smithy (5)

21 Organ piece, often preceded by toccata (5)

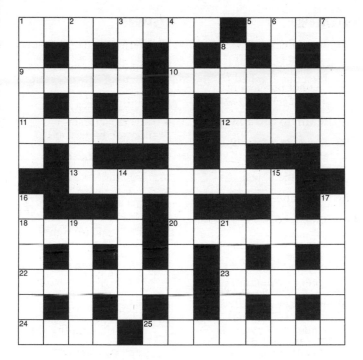

ACROSS

1 Bus-to-city-centre scheme (4,3,4)

7 Examination bed (5)

8 Swaggering courage (7)

10 Wave up and down (8)

11 Sound of geese, unhappy audience (4)

13 Symbolic object (6)

15 Lambert —, royal impostor; type of cake (6)

17 Wharf (4)

18 Imagines, theorises (8)

21 A wearing away (7)

22 Train of followers (5)

23 Undergo conversion (3,3,5)

DOWN

1 Vividly pretty (e.g. view) (11)

2 Circular; delivery route (5)

3 Sulky Trojan War hero (8)

4 Formal discussion (6)

5 Terrible czar (4)

6 Dishonest avoidance (7)

9 Becoming out of date (11)

12 Getting rid of; right to use (8)

14 Signal fires; Brecon has some (7)

16 Slake (thirst) (6)

19 Child's toy; be hanged (5)

20 Rub clean (4)

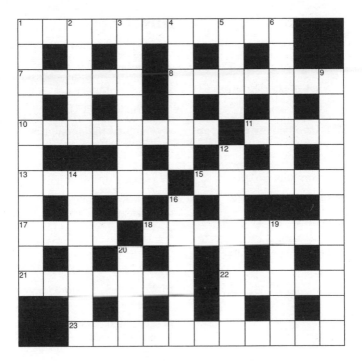

ACROSS

7 Big cat; small weight (5)

8 Range of colours (7)

9 Spot of condensation (7)

10 Making knot (5)

11 Fringe benefit; cheer (up) (4)

12 Tooth-strengthening water additive (8)

15 Definite; utter (8)

16 Arduous journey (4)

19 Devon/Cornwall boundary river (5)

21 Playhouse (7)

22 Batsman's turn (7)

23 Saltpetre (5)

DOWN

1 Display; delay (4,2)

2 Unconsciously (8)

3 (Art) category (5)

4 Food addict (7)

5 Ornamental needlecase (4)

6 West Indian music style (6)

8 Lands ruled from Vatican once (5,6)

13 Vex (8)

14 Looking daggers; obvious (error) (7)

15 First Irish county (alphabetically) (6)

17 Guardian, especially of museum collection (6)

18 Creature (5)

20 (Especially food) option list (4)

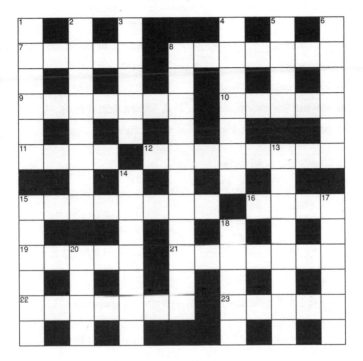

ACROSS

1 Chide (6)

7 Occur (6)

8 Little sketch, view (8)

10 Results; belongings (7)

11 SE Asia country, 1960s war with US (7)

12 Old Scots noble (5)

14 Vertical; very fine (5)

15 Mate its object (5)

19 Curative herb (7)

20 Cook up (7)

22 Oxygenating exercises (8)

23 Arthurian wizard (6)

24 Sounds like *feebly*; sort of magazine (6)

DOWN

1 Breathe new life into (6)

2 French stick (8)

3 Enthusiasm (8)

4 Professional cook (4)

5 Oration (6)

6 Church caretaker (6)

9 Unextreme (climate) (9)

12 The chronicler of Barset (8)

13 Printer's star (8)

16 Car horn; nose (*slang*) (6)

17 Island off Italy toe (6)

18 Shiny; sort of magazine (6)

21 Insincere, empty, talk (4)

ACROSS

1 Dull, disappointing episode (*joc.*) (8)

5 Fetter; James —, 007 (4)

8 In frail, insubstantial way (8)

9 Winged creature; prison (*slang*) (4)

11 Iron/carbon alloy; sounds like *pinch* (5)

12 Arise, flow (from) (7)

13 Mediaeval friar, pilgrim (6)

15 Apostate Roman emperor; type of calendar (6)

18 Element found in sand, computers (7)

19 Companion of Gog (5)

21 Giselle composer; water his ale (4)

22 Of the Great Flood (8)

23 Tax-deduction-at-source system (1,1,1,1)

24 Carer for flock (8)

DOWN

1 Elevates (5,2)

2 Patrick —, Australian Nobel author (5)

3 Bankrupt condition (10)

4 Latest winner of title (6)

6 Japanese paper modelling (7)

7 Jump out of way of (5)

10 Air-expelling machine (6,4)

14 Baby-soothing song (7)

16 Mildly, persistently, irritated (7)

17 Make wealthy (6)

18 On the dot (time); out of tune (5)

20 (False) appearance (5)

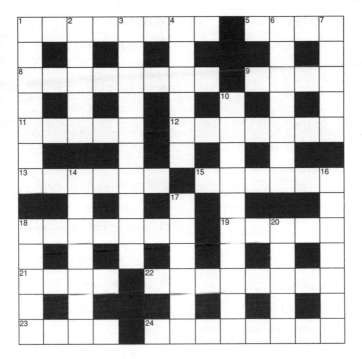

ACROSS

1 Academic, unwordly retreat (5,5)

8 Helps to rise; robbers' cry? (5,2)

9 The first disciple; — Bolivar (5)

10 Fighting tooth (4)

11 Enjoyable (8)

13 Strong loathing (6)

15 One ordained (6)

17 One eating all sorts of food (8)

18 Hasty; impetuous (4)

21 Seat; professorship (5)

22 Emphatic type (7)

23 Putting on best clothes; disguising (8,2)

DOWN

2 Goddess, planet (5)

3 Ploy (4)

4 Regular little drink (6)

5 Cleverclogs (8)

6 Disorderly search (7)

7 Laughing uncontrollably (2,8)

8 Jumble of items (10)

12 Wayward, contrary (8)

14 Isle of Man parliament (7)

16 Ancient Celtic 15s (6)

19 Farewell (5)

20 Principal; high seas (*poet.*) (4)

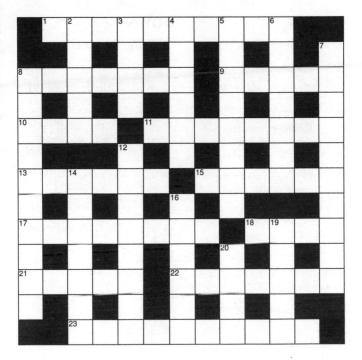

ACROSS

1 Happen together (8)

5 Of that nature (4)

8 Small (Scottish) farm (5)

9 Titivates; composes (5,2)

11 — Johnson, aviatrix; youngest of *Little Women* (3)

12 Old Harare; a Plain (9)

13 Go on board (6)

15 Rim, edge (6)

18 Recycleable-metal store (9)

19 Seed; *Great Expectations* hero (3)

20 Waves; paint spreaders (7)

21 2nd and 6th US presidents (5)

22 Tell of danger (4)

23 Install as king (8)

DOWN

1 Badge in hat (7)

2 Incongruity; mild sarcasm (5)

3 Calamitous reverse (11)

4 Little crease in chin (6)

6 Not reliable, not rigorous (7)

7 Joyful (5)

10 Friendly but fatal gesture (4,2,5)

14 Housebreaker (7)

16 Quick retort (7)

17 Plumlike tree (6)

18 Fastener; warder (*slang*) (5)

19 Socratic-dialogue author (5)

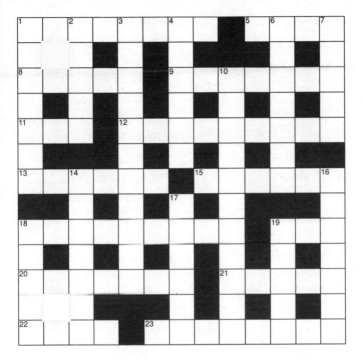

ACROSS

5 Main office (12)

8 Swiss breakfast "little mush" (6)

9 Devon grazing land; type of pony (6)

10 The 14 in *Othello* (4)

12 Soothe, hush (7)

14 Wicked man; criminal (7)

15 Greek *B* (4)

17 Industrial "action"; hit (6)

18 Bowman (6)

20 Disease; *far cleverest* (*anagram*) (7,5)

DOWN

1 Complacently superior; jingoistic (12)

2 Howls (at moon); coves (4)

3 Unsleeping (7)

4 Mad rush (8)

6 Little joke (4)

7 Brazil chief port (3,2,7)

11 Old lively dance (8)

13 Old and shrivelled (7)

16 Fifty percent (4)

19 Underground hollow; look out! (4)

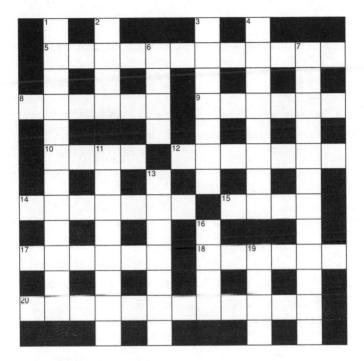

ACROSS

1 Self respect (*French*) (5,6)

8 Cambridge college; two Bible books (5)

9 In angry way (7)

10 (Archbishop of) York; a handicap race (4)

11 1815 victory (8)

13 Background, locale (6)

14 Killed (by mob); high on pot (6)

17 Melbourne state (8)

19 Stone particles; courage (4)

22 Pornography (7)

23 Rental agreement (5)

24 The Dominicans (5,6)

DOWN

1 Leg/foot joint (5)

2 Damaging blunder (3,4)

3 Hazard (4)

4 Of human types (6)

5 Character; possession (8)

6 Artist's stand (5)

7 Famous representative, example (6)

12 Speedwell; a cloth, a pass (8)

13 The films (US) (6)

15 Buddhist nothingness (7)

16 Act of air piracy (6)

18 (Southern) valley, hollow (5)

20 Lock of hair (5)

21 Indistinct sight (4)

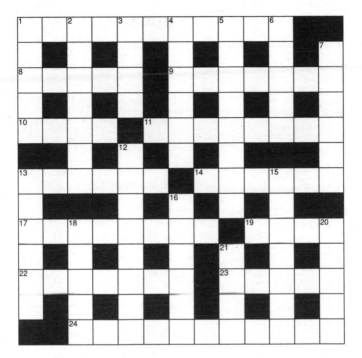

ACROSS

1 Philosopher, killed with hemlock (8)

5 Cock's crest; some honey (4)

9 Race for 1000, 2000 of them (7)

10 Linger (5)

11 Linger (4)

12 With pinkish plumage (7)

14 French white-wine region (6)

16 Counterbalance (6)

19 Remove deep dirt (7)

21 Offered; conceded (4)

24 Scottish landowner (5)

25 Wraith (7)

26 Out of danger (4)

27 Foot traveller (8)

DOWN

1 Indication, gesture (4)

2 Porcelain; mate (*slang*) (5)

3 Free of germs (7)

4 Make certain (6)

6 Joan of Arc its Maid (7)

7 Wagner festival town (8)

8 Probability; may go with *ends* (4)

13 Maths with infinitesimals (8)

15 Wild West policeman (7)

17 Cover for Adam and Eve (3,4)

18 Former Iran (6)

20 Naked; painting of one such (4)

22 Elector (5)

23 Try; listen to (4)

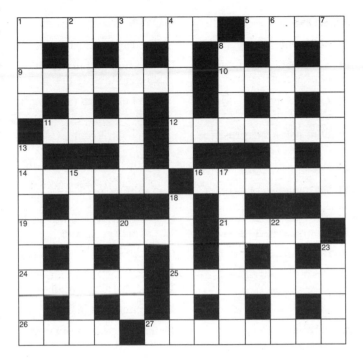

ACROSS

1 Shinbone (5)

4 Confused, slightly drunk (7)

8 *Cogito ergo sum* thinker (9)

9 Dull-coloured; press for payment (3)

10 Do winter sports (3)

11 Washerwoman (9)

12 Struggle, contest (5)

13 Soothe, put at rest (5)

16 Bow the knee (9)

18 Business end of pen (3)

20 Personality, selfishness (3)

21 A butterfly; *operating* (*anagram*) (6-3)

22 Foot lever (7)

23 Wood nymph (5)

DOWN

1 Daily sea movements (5)

2 Moistening (roast); sewing loosely (7)

3 No help at all (*sarcastic*) (1,3,3,2,4)

4 Irregular, patchy (6)

5 Handicapped (13)

6 Little house, especially for beavers (5)

7 Line of kings (7)

12 Invention (of the imagination) (7)

14 Protracted (7)

15 People in household (6)

17 Running knot (5)

19 Two-legged creature (5)

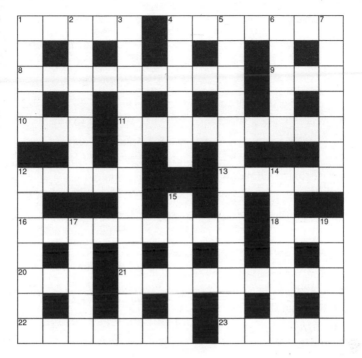

ACROSS

1 Oddments (4,3,6)

8 Handicraft with hooks (7)

9 Compel; violence (5)

10 Floor-cleaner; shock of hair (3)

11 Hostile reaction (8)

13 Regular, undeviant (6)

14 Difficulty; graze (6)

17 Special representative (8)

19 A cat; the piper's son (3)

21 South American "camel" (5)

22 Reading desk (7)

24 Becomes attached to place (4,4,5)

DOWN

1 Attractive; turning into (8)

2 Cavalryman (7)

3 Tree; burnt residue (3)

4 To separate (6)

5 (Hunt) hot on trail (2,4,3)

6 (Especially military) functional unit (5)

7 Tool store (4)

11 E.g. colliery musicians (5,4)

12 End of the line (8)

15 30s movement; *redcoat* (*anagram*) (3,4)

16 Left uncultivated (6)

18 Intended (5)

20 Undergarment; error (4)

23 Mangy dog (3)

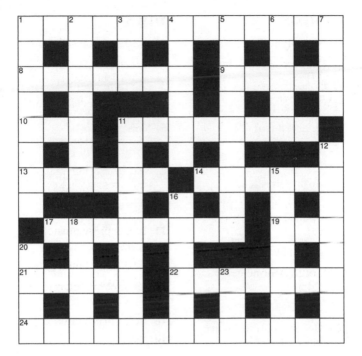

ACROSS

7 Friendly (12)

9 Lady's room (7)

10 Concentrated fire (5)

11 Bird; bar (4)

12 Indebted (to) (8)

15 Trilby's master (*du Maurier*) (8)

17 Muslim mystic (4)

19 Turn, rotate; one that does (5)

21 Traveller; US space probe (7)

22 Force to cooperate (5,4,3)

DOWN

1 Gushingly emotional (8)

2 Greek fabulist (5)

3 Die of hunger (6)

4 *War and Peace* author (7)

5 Nobleman (4)

6 Scout around (11)

8 Mid-Welsh university town, resort (11)

13 Chores (8)

14 Nimbleness (7)

16 Source of (especially vicar's) income (6)

18 Romany (5)

20 Send forth (4)

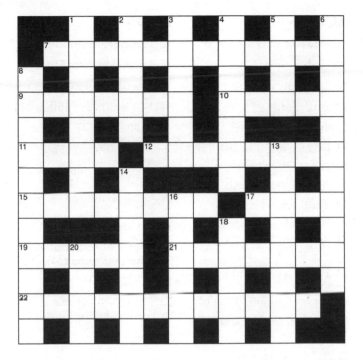

ACROSS

1 Preserve in brine; naughty child (6)

4 Explosive-carrying plane (6)

9 A blend; (especially dentist's) alloy (7)

10 Drink (one's) health (5)

11 Gurkha knife (5)

13 (Shady) share of profit (4-3)

14 Headgear; stopper (3)

15 Different, alternative (5)

16 Pulse seed; a *sweet* flower (3)

17 A god; a liquid metal (7)

19 Change, move; spell of work (5)

21 *Balance* star-sign (5)

22 Connector plug (7)

24 Silly laugh (6)

25 Fraud, cheating (6)

DOWN

1 Sawn length (5)

2 Break down; extol (5,2)

3 Carry awkwardly; sort of sail, of worm (3)

5 Fringes (of town) (9)

6 Well done! (5)

7 A liqueur; almond biscuit (7)

8 *Rubáiyát* author (4,7)

12 Give protective jab (9)

14 King Arthur's court (7)

16 Love potion; sounds like *strainer* (7)

18 Automaton (5)

20 Fortune-telling cards (5)

23 Reverent fear (3)

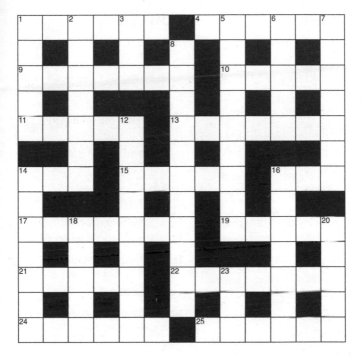

ACROSS

1 Think over (8)

5 (Skin) flake off; fruit skin (4)

7 Rodent, losing out to grey cousin (3,8)

8 Ambush; snare (4)

9 Olympic city, 2004 (6)

10 Proficient people (6)

13 Play on words (3)

14 Rotatory force (6)

17 Game tile with spots (6)

18 Gave temporarily (4)

19 Jewish linked-triangle motif (4,2,5)

20 Brawl; start to wear (4)

21 Idle type (8)

DOWN

1 Compare unlike features (8)

2 (Liquid) ooze out (4)

3 Cheeky (13)

4 Crude but adequate (5-3-5)

5 Conditional early release (6)

6 All leave (*stage direction*) (6)

7 Somewhat; for preference (6)

11 Self-possessed; balanced (6)

12 Quick way (5-3)

15 Ejection; *sure to* (*anagram*) (6)

16 Excavation pit; one hunted (6)

18 E.g. wing, flipper, leg (4)

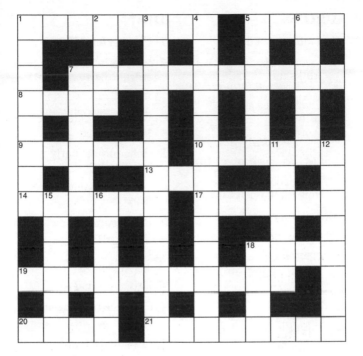

ACROSS

1 Totally unused (5,3)
7 Cover (with cloth) (5)
8 A Franciscan monk (4,5)
9 A spread; a nasty position (3)
10 Use voice; confess (4)
11 Bad luck; its bringer (6)
13 Hindu god, with Brahma, Shiva (6)
14 Moderate; a maggot (6)
17 Fruit in Chekhov's Orchard (6)
18 Animal; centre of target (4)
20 Conflict (3)
22 Of hairdressing (9)
23 Requirements (5)
24 Horrible-looking; (US) thug (4-4)

DOWN

1 Counterfeit (5)
2 Roman lake, underworld entrance; *van user* (*anagram*) (7)
3 A pudding; faulty (4)
4 Magazine head (6)
5 Concert-party instrument (5)
6 Mound-building insect (7)
7 Bed-clearing vessel (7)
12 Puts inside (7)
13 Watching (e.g. TV) (7)
15 Driving round (7)
16 Clifton Bridge designer (6)
17 Pitiless (5)
19 Sweet on stick; money (*slang*) (5)
21 Dinner signal; award (*slang*) (4)

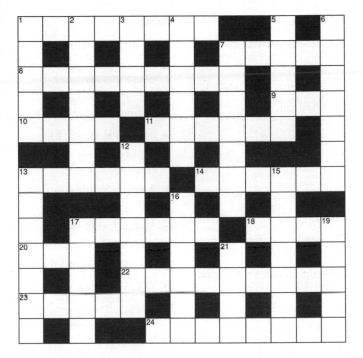

ACROSS

6 One leaving work on the dot (5,7)

7 Unspeaking (6)

8 Dark and sad (6)

9 A fruit, sounds like *dim-witted* (4)

10 Unpaid (officer) (8)

12 One-cell tiny organisms (8)

16 Poor dwelling (4)

18 Old thing to pack up troubles in (6)

20 Peak (6)

21 By chance (12)

DOWN

1 Change of position; campaign (8)

2 Quick drawing (6)

3 Strongman shorn by Delilah (6)

4 A swindle (4)

5 Panic; a *Reign* of it, 1794 (6)

6 A cold; to cool (5)

11 Be like (8)

13 (Allotted) for each person (6)

14 Teased; unjustified (margin) (6)

15 Advantages (6)

17 Concord; the number one (5)

19 Runny French cheese (4)

ACROSS

1 Hurl; indulgent spell (5)

7 Documented; formally but not practically (2,5)

8 Distinction; bullet diameter (7)

9 Doncaster classic (2,5)

11 Twain hero; sounds like *type of bean* (6)

13 Annual admission of income (3,6)

15 Non-government warship (9)

19 Aptitude; ancient money (6)

21 Rifle-fixed stabber (7)

23 Clumsy (7)

24 Defer to another time (7)

25 Come in; write down (5)

DOWN

1 Concentrate (on) (5)

2 Partner's family (2-4)

3 Gallows (6)

4 Carries out; some deer (4)

5 Dormant; potentially there (6)

6 Boisterous partying (7)

10 At which to aim (6)

12 Baby's toy; loose-component noise (6)

14 V. Woolf novel; — Furioso (*Ariosto*) (7)

16 Haitian animism (6)

17 Fester (6)

18 Meal, food (6)

20 Royal house of Henry VII (5)

22 Armoured vehicle; fuel holder (4)

ACROSS

1 London entertainment district (4)

3 Absorbed; wholly underwater (8)

9 Push on, forward (5)

10 — Monroe (7)

11 Hamlet died in his arms (7)

12 Wide-mouth pitcher (4)

14 Sudden (6)

16 Slowly simmered (6)

18 Well-known actor (4)

19 Determine, declare (7)

22 Three kings, one "wicked" (7)

23 Russian buckwheat pancake (5)

24 Noise-reducer (in car, gun) (8)

25 Shivering fit (4)

DOWN

1 Shaven yob (8)

2 Too ready to complain (13)

4 Wealth (as a god) (6)

5 A pledge; serious (7)

6 Couple's twenty-fifth anniversary (6,7)

7 Take formal meal (4)

8 Dull; a place to live (4)

13 Sticky substance (8)

15 Be relevant (7)

17 Deal with; touch (6)

20 Employment; may be for the boys (4)

21 Rainbow goddess; part of eye (4)

TIMES 2 CROSSWORD 54

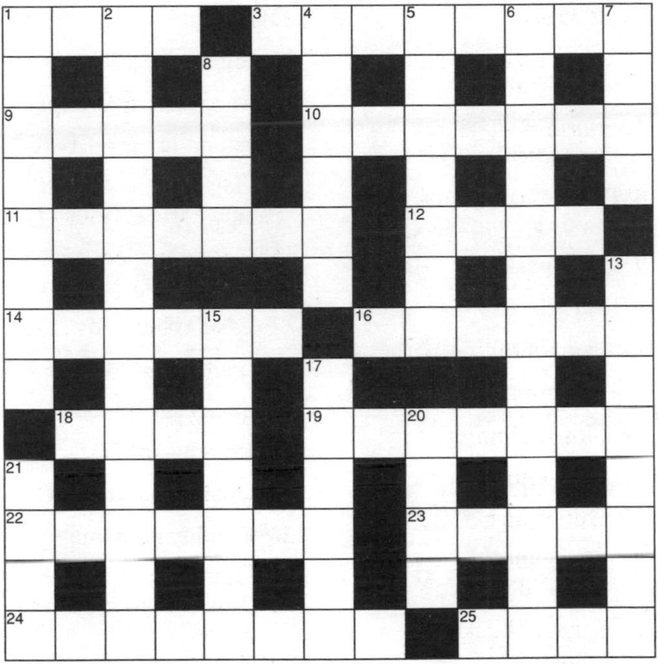

ACROSS

1 Mock; supply (to hotel room) (4,2)

5 Fruit; Peter —, mechanical (*MND*) (6)

8 Piece of computer; wood shaving (4)

9 Dampness (8)

10 Referee (6)

12 Smell strongly (4)

15 Crossing-place to execution (Venice) (6,2,5)

16 March tiredly; hit wildly (4)

17 Not illegal (6)

19 Height (8)

21 Fibre; old invading German (4)

22 One from Nairobi (6)

23 Long, angry speech (6)

DOWN

2 Short-lived (9)

3 Drop; pickpocket (3)

4 Treated luxuriously (8)

5 Question and answer game (4)

6 Meeting for job applicant (9)

7 Motor vehicle (3)

11 Minor humiliation (9)

13 Tired out; spent (9)

14 Well off (8)

18 Disaster; bankruptcy (4)

20 Fib; relax (3)

21 Judder; container (3)

ACROSS

1 Inconsiderate (9)

6 Swan; horse; loaf; pipe (3)

8 Shop surface; measurer (7)

9 Suite; conveyance (5)

10 Piece of news; likewise (4)

11 Pristine; unhackneyed (8)

13 Ribbon of 17 *dn* (6)

14 Fisherman with line (6)

17 Overfussy (8)

18 Pound; chewing tobacco (4)

20 Thin; have mercy on (5)

21 Foreign; unusual (7)

22 Expert; a card (3)

23 Rapidly grows (9)

DOWN

1 Ointment; soothing suavity (7)

2 Very famous person (9,4)

3 Behind; dead (4)

4 Uproar (6)

5 One suing (8)

6 England/France connection (7,6)

7 Hackneyed (5)

12 World War 1 poppy site; Anne of Cleves its mare (8)

15 Richard —, *Oklahoma!* composer (7)

16 Humiliating disaster (6)

17 Italian dough (5)

19 Crustacean; an apple (4)

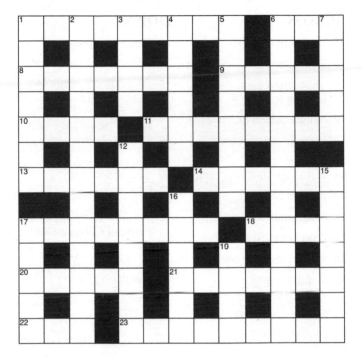

ACROSS

1 Supervise exam (10)
8 Word such as *NATO*, *laser* (7)
9 Cutting tool (5)
10 Hit; pare; film extract (4)
11 Vacuous waffle (8)
13 Hotel lobby (5)
14 Jape; edible-bud shrub (5)
16 Informal interview programme (4,4)
17 Fruit fibre; essence (4)
20 Making good sense (5)
21 Rope; artist (7)
22 Final battle (*Revelation*) (10)

DOWN

1 Son of Abraham (5)
2 Oxbridge contest (7,5)
3 Heredity unit (4)
4 Unwanted furniture (6)
5 Withdraw, recover (4,4)
6 Frustrated, let down (12)
7 Shooting star (6)
12 Fighter for cause (8)
13 Capricious (6)
15 Fairground game (4-2)
18 Grey/white wader (5)
19 Penalty; clear, dry (4)

57

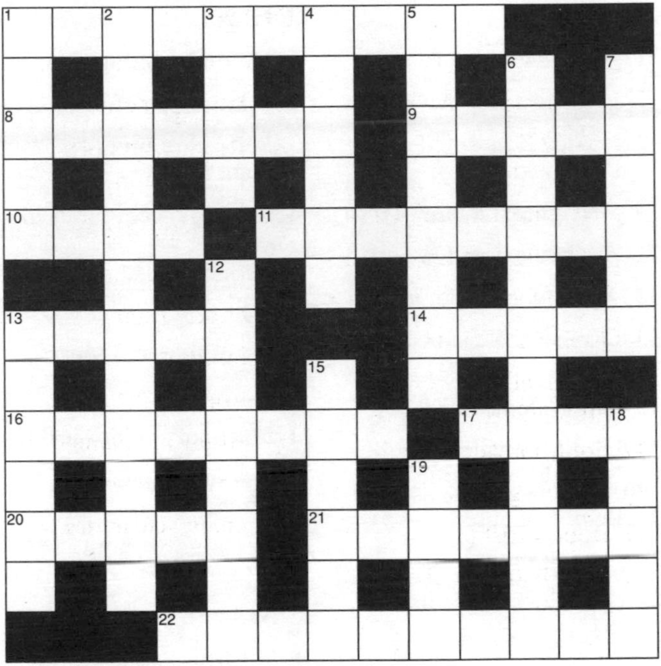

ACROSS

1 Always in same role (8)

5 Light-focusing device (4)

9 Huxley future-hell novel (5,3,5)

10 Stronghold; retain (4)

11 Eye protectors (7)

13 Agreement; harmony (6)

15 Disfigure; old squeezer (6)

18 Supplement to will (7)

20 Lavish, succulent (growth); alcoholic (4)

23 Be dishonoured (4,4,5)

24 Burden (4)

25 (E.g. clock's) oscillator (8)

DOWN

1 Mr Punch's dog (4)

2 Chatter idly (5)

3 Soft-soled shoe; plant like ivy (7)

4 Conveyance; sounds like *kill* (6)

6 Personal sound-stopper (7)

7 Move to avoid (4-4)

8 Gulp (4)

12 Imaginary; whimsical (8)

14 C-softening mark (*French*) (7)

16 Declared without evidence (7)

17 Niche (6)

19 Hit with hand; part of shirt (4)

21 Threatening look, growl; tangle (5)

22 Ray; timber support (4)

ACROSS

1 Afternoon meal (4,3)

5 A fish; (bird) sit (5)

8 Little wood (5)

9 Fired clay (article) (7)

10 Poisonous snake (3)

11 *Oedipus Rex* playwright (9)

12 Depressing; economics such a science (*Carlyle*) (6)

14 Half an island; one man in a boat (*Jerome*) (6)

17 Briefly return for contact (5,4)

18 Peat-growing area (3)

19 Post-mortem (7)

20 (Sheep) feed; abrasion (5)

21 Poem of lament (5)

22 Overlook; disregard (7)

DOWN

1 Drawn; Rider —, author (7)

2 Band, collection (5)

3 Fasten; cup game (3)

4 Receive (6)

5 Slowly strain through (9)

6 A walker; a rose (7)

7 Pawns; horse's ankles (5)

11 Cheerfully careless (4-5)

13 Run (away); sink (ship) (7)

15 Portion; part of line (*maths*) (7)

16 (US) ravine (6)

17 Make gentle fun of (5)

18 Mark on horse; burn (5)

20 Joke; silence (3)

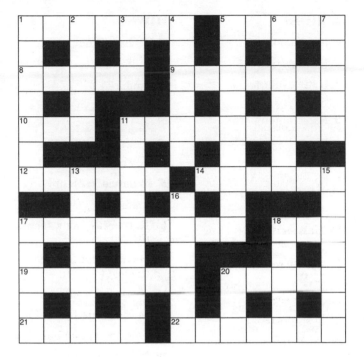

ACROSS

1 Ideal world (6)

5 In footwear (4)

9 Utterly unoriginal (copy) (7)

10 Radio antenna (6)

11 Instinctive (reaction) (4-4)

12 Be tangible expression of (6)

15 Barred grid, screen (6)

18 Speaking little (8)

20 Animal shed; solidly based (6)

22 Rider's foot support (7)

23 Broken in; boring (4)

24 Expel from country (6)

DOWN

2 Herbal infusion (6)

3 Calm, undisturbed (8)

4 Similar (5)

6 One due to succeed (4)

7 Require, insist (6)

8 Cocktail mixer; US sectarian (6)

13 To flatter (6,2)

14 Loathe (6)

16 Glass vessel; witty answer (6)

17 Appropriate, correct (6)

19 Youngster (5)

21 Edge; to be very full (4)

ACROSS

1 Serious setback (4-4)

5 Stout string (4)

8 Financially ruined (8)

9 Refuse (authority) (4)

11 Glaring, sensational (5)

12 Mechanism-damaging imp (7)

13 Render ineffective (6)

15 Urge forward (6)

18 Very light, eggy dish (7)

19 French currency (5)

21 (Official) gown (4)

22 The ordinary bloke (8)

23 A river; sounds like *drinks* (4)

24 A stiffened muslin (8)

DOWN

1 Hanging Gardens city (7)

2 Kind giver (5)

3 Idle and fed up (5,5)

4 Attack, question (in argument) (6)

6 Partly coincide (7)

7 Senior member (of corps) (5)

10 Solid land (5,5)

14 Mutter complaints (7)

16 Unbridled freedom; a permit (7)

17 River creature; apprentice Scout (6)

18 Strengthening bar; walk proudly (5)

20 Carrying weapon (5)

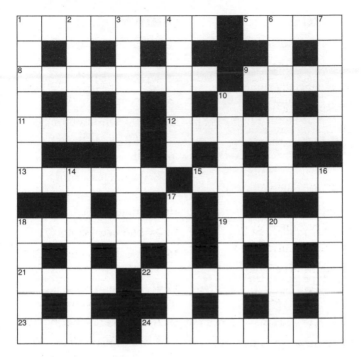

ACROSS

1 Fortuitous; offhand (6)

4 Part of e.g. cauliflower head (6)

8 Horrid, contemptible (4)

9 Left-handed fighter (8)

10 In free, romantic effusion; *drip chaos* (*anagram*) (9)

13 In strange way (5)

15 (Woman) well-built (5)

16 Ground, founding principle (5)

18 Permission (to land); type of sale (9)

21 Wary (8)

22 A drink; a naval town (4)

23 Inter-state agreement (6)

24 Not far off (6)

DOWN

1 Prance around (6)

2 Content of (school) course (8)

3 Rope with noose (5)

5 One not on time (9)

6 Absorbed, carried away (4)

7 Vulgar, trashy (6)

11 Below the line (character) (9)

12 Southern US; cooking pot (5)

14 Heavy shower (8)

16 Animal as lion, tiger (3,3)

17 Vicar's robing-room (6)

19 Malicious ignition (5)

20 Smoke, e.g. with anger (4)

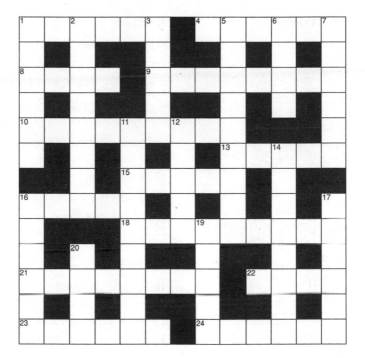

ACROSS

1 West Indian citrus fruit (4)

4 Leonid —, 70s USSR chief (8)

8 Endurance; G. & S. operetta (8)

9 Drink too much (4)

10 Relax; area of authority (5)

11 Of the stars (7)

13 Responsible (for crime) (6)

15 Way of speaking; mark over letter (6)

18 Sailors' spear (7)

20 Antipodean soldier (5)

23 Yugoslav dictator (4)

24 Rain protector (8)

25 Tobias —, *Random*, *Pickle* author (8)

26 Two-master; a jolly-boat (4)

DOWN

2 Fruit; type of shot (5)

3 First (letter) (7)

4 Rely; riverside (4)

5 Occurring in due course (8)

6 Commercial lodging (5)

7 Make clear (7)

10 Apparatus; equip (vessel) (3)

12 The focus of all eyes (8)

14 Element U (7)

16 Tinned-goods factory (7)

17 Nervous twitch (3)

19 Move around looking for prey (5)

21 Give permission for (5)

22 Be right next to (4)

ACROSS

1 Yellow-skin disease (8)

5 Lapdog (*abbr.*); sounds like *summit* (4)

9 Blunder (5)

10 Edible plant; nonsense (7)

11 Hermione's husband (*Winter's Tale*) (7)

12 Irritable; Mole's friend (*Grahame*) (5)

13 Dostoevsky's Brothers (9)

18 Of the same value (5)

20 Sheet with cut pattern (7)

22 Old hospital welfare officer (7)

23 Vex (5)

24 Longer forearm bone (4)

25 Towards the sunset (8)

DOWN

1 Keep balls in air (6)

2 Degrade (priest) (7)

3 Lived (in); lingered (on) (5)

4 Seasonal fir (9,4)

6 Forcibly obtain; precise (5)

7 Post-conception stage (6)

8 Sort of glass, of watch (6)

14 Charlemagne knight, Oliver rival (6)

15 Italian home of Palladio (7)

16 Sense of reliving a scene (4,2)

17 Took part in game, drama (6)

19 Deprive (chap) of courage (5)

21 Glorify (5)

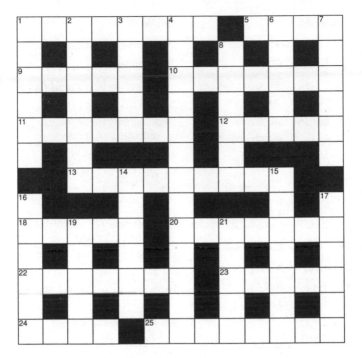

ACROSS

1 Fulcrum (5)

4 Fetched (7)

8 Kerry town, near lakes (9)

9 Period, epoch (3)

10 Actual (4)

11 Courtly dances (8)

13 Chain for animal (6)

14 Drenched (6)

17 Consummate skill (8)

19 Twin of Jacob (*Genesis*) (4)

22 Oz bird; EU project (3)

23 E.g. house paint; specious excuses (9)

24 Improve appeal of (7)

25 Albrecht —, engraver (5)

DOWN

1 A rod; a betting game (5)

2 Doughty (7)

3 Jewel-in-head creature (4)

4 *Pilgrim's Progress* author (6)

5 Conjunction-of-opposites device (*rhetoric*) (8)

6 Huge man (5)

7 Betrayal (7)

12 *I got Rhythm* composer (8)

13 Swinging bar (7)

15 Hopelessness (7)

16 Mark of blow (6)

18 Verity (5)

20 Deferentially escort (5)

21 Notice (paid) (4)

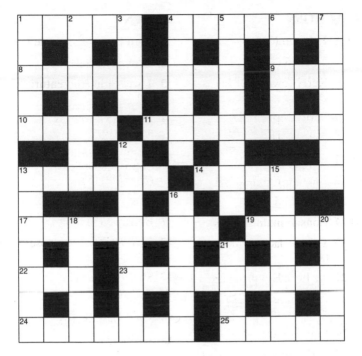

ACROSS

2 Bridgetown its capital (8)

6 Bargain over price (6)

8 Area of authority, of expertise (6)

9 One raised (*John*); a beggar (*Luke*) (7)

10 Aroma trail (5)

12 Merchant sailing ship (10)

16 (Chair) padding (10)

18 Conscious (of) (5)

20 Throb, oscillate (7)

21 Water down (6)

22 Land for crops (6)

23 Confusion; ailment (8)

DOWN

1 First man into space (7)

2 Leave (in will) (8)

3 Lady's top (6)

4 First Englishman round world (5)

5 An upper house (6)

7 Majesty; God's — (*Hopkins*) (8)

11 Judgment yardsticks (8)

13 Unit of air pressure (8)

14 Liable to snap (7)

15 Came down; sort of gentry (6)

17 Annoy, bother (6)

19 African range; sort of book (5)

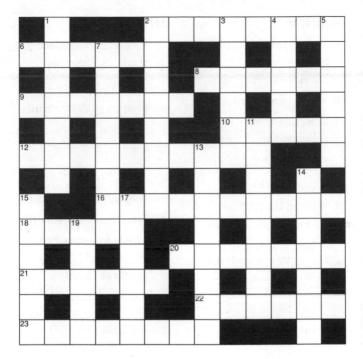

ACROSS

7 Earnest prayer (12)

9 Macbeth told to *beware* him (7)

10 Steal; cook slowly (5)

11 Ship, its frame (4)

12 Belonging to C. of E. (8)

15 Painting of clouds (8)

17 Aspersion (4)

19 Wall under pitched roof (5)

21 Adjudications (7)

22 Huge (like interstellar distance) (12)

DOWN

1 A trade; carnage (8)

2 Poppy drug (5)

3 Light (Indian) meal (6)

4 Young frog (7)

5 Capital of Peru (4)

6 Witch (11)

8 American Indian message; *Mike's slogan* (*anagram*) (5,6)

13 Dated event list (8)

14 Level, rank; staggered formation (7)

16 Length of time (6)

18 Elderly person (*slang*) (5)

20 (Fish) take bait (4)

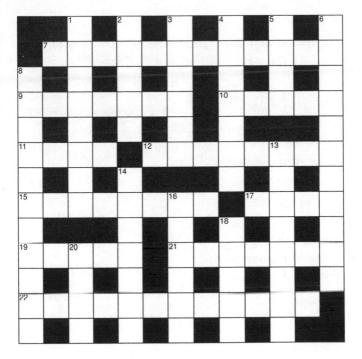

ACROSS

1 Special assault unit (8)

5 Complacent (4)

9 Spiral of disaster (7,6)

10 Horseback game (4)

11 Mariners' star-angle measurer (7)

13 One dying for cause (6)

15 Conceal; front of TV (6)

18 Giant David killed (7)

20 Before (4-); a stake (4)

23 Shaw play; *madman – he rants* (*anagram*) (4,3,3,3)

24 Use keyboard (4)

25 Natation (8)

DOWN

1 South American guinea-pig (4)

2 Aggressively masculine (5)

3 Expression of regret (7)

4 Cease (from) (6)

6 Ornamental cord knotting (7)

7 Saying hello to (8)

8 Hoodoo (4)

12 One going to live abroad (8)

14 Pickled herring fillet (7)

16 Kent port; Pitt its Earl (7)

17 Follow closely, secretly (6)

19 Not quite closed (4)

21 Musical speeds (5)

22 Catch (clothes); minor hiccup (4)

ACROSS

7 Grain husks (4)

8 From the East (8)

9 Feelers (8)

10 Uriah —, Dickens's cringer (4)

11 Jean-Paul —, French existentialist (6)

13 A hat; a cricketer (6)

15 Slow (movement) (6)

17 Car repair shop (6)

19 Textile frame; impend (4)

21 Charge on house (8)

23 Peaceful (8)

24 Wound-dressing fabric (4)

DOWN

1 An inebriate (8)

2 Put money (into) (6)

3 Planted (4)

4 An assortment (5,3)

5 In no special way (6)

6 Be indolent (4)

12 Gigantic (8)

14 Taking on; attractive (8)

16 Playing at casino (6)

18 Ply, entertain well (6)

20 Monster (4)

22 Irk (4)

ACROSS

3 Town where Jesus grew up (8)

7 Adjust; sounds like *a melody* (6)

8 A sweet; nonsense (6)

9 Sharply stylish (clothes) (*slang*) (6)

10 Overwhelm with light (6)

11 Stare steadily (4)

13 Instant, flash (5)

15 Harmful insect (4)

17 Sharp double bend (6)

18 Showy type of rhododendron (6)

19 Food store (6)

20 Rub gently with nose (6)

21 Set off (bomb) (8)

DOWN

1 Verse of poem (6)

2 Eat like pig (6)

3 January 1 (3,4)

4 To hero-worship (7)

5 Steal employer's funds (8)

6 French Protestant (8)

11 Greying; cried fretfully (8)

12 (Babylonian) stepped pyramid (8)

13 Exchange (old for new) (5,2)

14 Paul —, Post-Impressionist (7)

15 Italian square (6)

16 Fitting, proper (6)

ACROSS

1 Shipshape (4)

3 Blameworthy (8)

8 Abu Simbel pharaoh; *mere ass?* (*anagram*) (7)

10 A daisy plant (2-3)

11 Pop-music-writing district (3,3,5)

13 German art songs (6)

15 Entertained (6)

17 Travelling (teacher) (11)

20 Lean veal-neck (end); to 1 *dn* (5)

21 Appearing before judge (2,5)

22 17th century Protestant sect (8)

23 Catcall (4)

DOWN

1 Strangle; sort of valve (8)

2 Evil spirit (5)

4 Remove (rider, MP) (6)

5 Causing difficulties (11)

6 Farewells; (baby's) sleep (3-4)

7 At any time (4)

9 Pre-performance panic (5,6)

12 Teacher (8)

14 Ruler; Beethoven's fifth piano concerto (7)

16 Possible choice (6)

18 Temporary cease-fire agreement (5)

19 At earliest convenience (*abbr.*) (4)

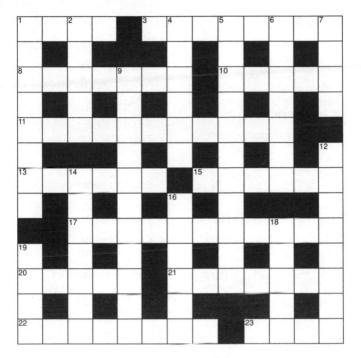

ACROSS

1 Curve; sort of galaxy, of staircase (6)

5 Type of ink, club; an ocean (6)

8 Nasty smell (*slang*) (4)

9 Answer impertinently (4,4)

10 Lower (6)

12 Strange; very (*Scots.*) (4)

15 Be utterly ruthless (4,2,7)

16 Anonymous; Lady Jane — (4)

17 Fairy king (*MND*) (6)

19 Deep-freezing-the-dead science (8)

21 Ominous; disastrous (4)

22 Mediterranean island, south of Turkey (6)

23 (Hair) shaped; (person) titled (6)

DOWN

2 Film-playing device (9)

3 Scrap (of cloth); piece of syncopated music (3)

4 Able to read (8)

5 Lazy, unemployed (4)

6 One of dissipated life (9)

7 Part of circle (3)

11 Cheap-drink time (5,4)

13 Crowd; open space for gathering (9)

14 Giant statue (8)

18 Student lodgings; barbed remarks (4)

20 A fish; a beam (3)

21 Forget one's lines (3)

ACROSS

1 Release (prisoner);
   fire (gun) (9)
6 Tricked; owned (3)
8 Break in line of verse (7)
9 Augustus —, Victorian
   Gothic architect (5)
10 Someone tricked (4)
11 Only-one-wife/husband
   system (8)
13 Plan, system; plot (6)
14 Bring to conclusion;
   tease (*slang*) (4,2)
17 Ill-defined; vague (8)
18 Small (skirt, computer)
   (4)
20 Set of steps (5)
21 Inspired predictor (7)
22 Induced; was in front (3)
23 One tearing down;
   a warship (9)

DOWN

1 Makes mind up (7)
2 Win everything (5,3,5)
3 Lug; booty (4)
4 Excuse; logic (6)
5 Wild joy (8)
6 Arrogant (4-3-6)
7 Dark and dirty (5)
12 Earnestly pleaded (8)
15 Lecturer's stick; gun dog
   (7)
16 A brawl (6)
17 Of the nose (5)
19 Grimly obstinate (4)

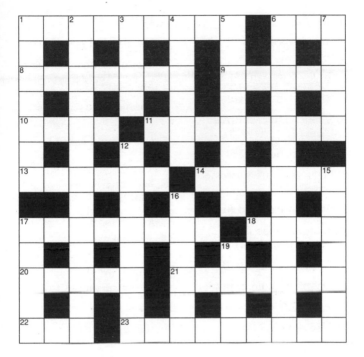

ACROSS

1 In advance (10)

7 Annul (7)

8 Demand (one's rights) (5)

10 French novelist, wrote *Gigi* (7)

11 Be of benefit (5)

12 Season Keats addressed (6)

15 Prevent from leaving (6)

17 German World War 2 submarine (1-4)

18 Drug from hemp (7)

21 Aristocrat; old coin (5)

22 Heartfelt, expressive (7)

23 The old days (10)

DOWN

1 Herb in Keats's pot (5)

2 Welsh town; a stone (5)

3 Save; buy back (6)

4 Foreign measure, over two acres (7)

5 US/Canada Falls (7)

6 Keats's Attic pot (7,3)

9 Sad state Keats addressed (10)

13 Problem; to worry (7)

14 Annual car inspection (3,4)

16 Engraver; another (different) drink (6)

19 Froth (5)

20 Make deduction (5)

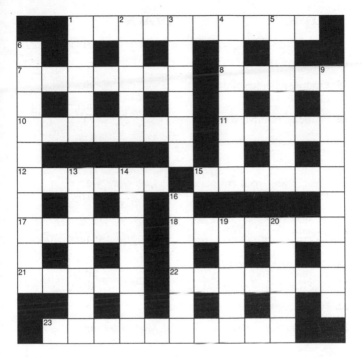

ACROSS

1 Easy skill; (US) plant (8)

5 Washtub; a city (4)

9 Counterproductive consoler (4,9)

10 Andean country (4)

11 Unenthusiastic, feeble (7)

13 Respond (6)

15 One living from robbery (6)

18 Notion (7)

20 John —, composer; barred enclosure (4)

23 Hamlet's question (2,2,2,3,2,2)

24 Labyrinth (4)

25 He does one's dirty work (8)

DOWN

1 Pacific ex-British republic (4)

2 Hawser; electricity wire (5)

3 Academic talk; scolding (7)

4 Disorderly din (6)

6 Amaze (7)

7 Genetic transmission from parents (8)

8 Benefit; close (companion) (4)

12 Man of all work (8)

14 Entertainment industry (7)

16 One severely self-denying (7)

17 Attitude (mental, physical) (6)

19 Sailors' diluted rum (4)

21 Darkness, misery (5)

22 Depend (on); spare (4)

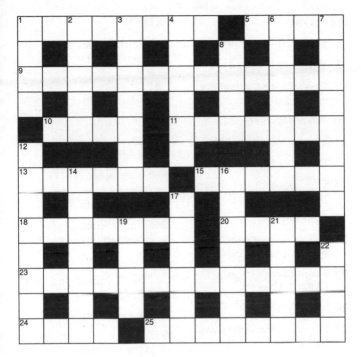

ACROSS

1 Emblems of royalty (7)
5 Mad (dog) (5)
8 Sudden spurt; exploded (5)
9 Advantage (7)
10 Deep crack in ice (8)
11 Part of eye; to hit; to fasten (4)
13 Signature album (9,4)
16 Applaud (4)
17 Block before house; close, on one's (8)
20 *Manon Lescaut* composer (7)
21 Indian police stick (5)
22 Coarse mineral used for polishing (5)
23 Saying *th* for *s* (7)

DOWN

1 Manderley book (*du Maurier*) (7)
2 Furze (5)
3 Lassitude (8)
4 Relating to envoys (13)
5 Official position; smelling off (4)
6 An ox; a bison (7)
7 To dump; a channel (5)
12 Laughs delightedly (8)
14 Instalment (of e.g. loan) (7)
15 *Mandalay* poet (7)
16 Spinney (5)
18 All play (*music*) (5)
19 Thin but strong (person) (4)

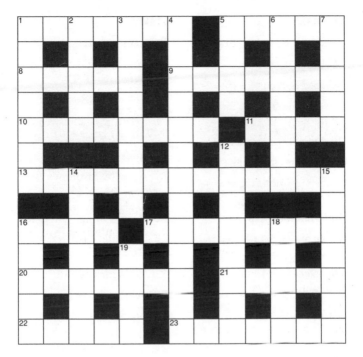

ACROSS

1 Brood, be sullen (4)

3 Rough comic verses (8)

8 Land force (4)

9 Wheedle a loan (8)

11 The wrong crowd to mix with (3,7)

14 Say from memory (6)

15 Corrupt behaviour (6)

17 Within reach; easy to understand (10)

20 Feeble person (8)

21 Therefore; monster (*reversed*) (4)

22 Physically real (8)

23 Contradict (4)

DOWN

1 Sword sheath (8)

2 One wounded, ineffective (4,4)

4 Take possession of, fill (6)

5 Without basis (10)

6 Tirade (4)

7 Edible bulb; sounds like *liquid escape* (4)

10 *Primavera* artist (10)

12 Scout gathering (8)

13 Ritual (8)

16 Edible part of nut (6)

18 Squash (fly) (4)

19 Win; profit (4)

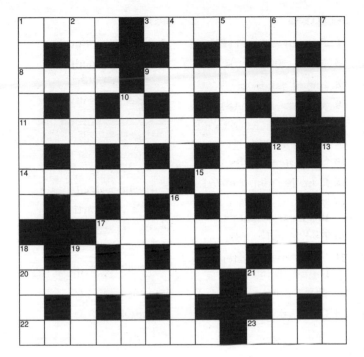

ACROSS

1 German emperor title (6)

5 Giving off reek (6)

8 Part of guitar; worry (4)

9 Window-cleaner's scraper (8)

10 Overall chief (7)

11 Grind (teeth) (5)

13 In malcontented mood (11)

16 Certificate; wallet (*archaic*) (5)

18 Temporary expedient (7)

21 Diffuse through (8)

22 Statue worshipped (4)

23 Salvage (6)

24 Circular; plump (6)

DOWN

2 Unable to float off (7)

3 Indian stringed instrument (5)

4 Remembrance herb (8)

5 Retained portion of ticket (4)

6 Never-ending; Rome this city (7)

7 Fertile, wind-deposited dust (5)

12 Woolly clothing (8)

14 Of earthquakes (7)

15 Cavalryman; to coerce (7)

17 Crinkly fabric; pancake (5)

19 Produce hard copy (5)

20 Bag; set of arguments (4)

ACROSS

1 Tack; prompt payment, on it (4)

3 Administrative assistant officer (8)

9 Essential (5)

10 Shoe repairer; an iced drink (7)

11 To a large extent (7)

12 An instant; give eye signal (4)

14 Hypnotised state (6)

16 Hateful (6)

18 An animal; put up with (4)

19 Bullfight horseman (7)

22 Arousing strong feeling (7)

23 *Goodbye, Mr —; — with Everything* (5)

24 Earnest plea (8)

25 A crony of Falstaff (4)

DOWN

1 Find the route (8)

2 Suffering together (2,3,4,4)

4 Metrical foot, *tum-ti-ti* (6)

5 (Head bloodied but) erect (7)

6 In due course (3,2,4,4)

7 Mountain pool (4)

8 Strip (in e.g. blind) (4)

13 Strong-coffee method (8)

15 Joined-up (writing) (7)

17 Optimistic (6)

20 Bird; set (gun) ready to fire (4)

21 Charity event; to entertain lavishly (4)

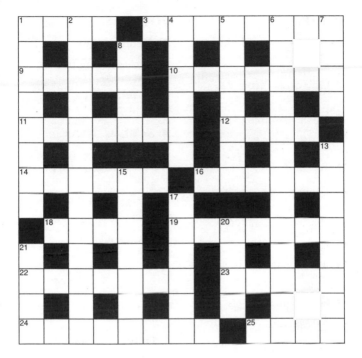

ACROSS

1 Silent waterbird (4,4)

5 Food in shell; crazy (4)

9 One calved from e.g. Antarctic (7)

10 River mammal (5)

11 A fish; singe (4)

12 More strong and healthy (7)

14 Send to custody before trial (6)

16 Correct (manuscript) again (6)

19 School bag (7)

21 Agitate (4)

24 Of less importance (5)

25 Deathly drinks (7)

26 Protest march (4)

27 Lets go (8)

DOWN

1 To cripple (4)

2 Parts of body, of gear wheel (5)

3 (E.g. candle) fat; *nastier* (*anagram*) (7)

4 South-west African country (6)

6 Never tested; still on 14? (7)

7 Women's club (*especially US*) (8)

8 Throw up (coin, pancake) (4)

13 Took for granted; took liberties (8)

15 Part for whole, as *rod* for *angler* (7)

17 (Bath) attached to bedroom (2,5)

18 (Time) pass (6)

20 Five-year-old male deer (4)

22 Presses; fetters (5)

23 Wife/sister of Osiris (4)

THE SOLUTIONS

1

2

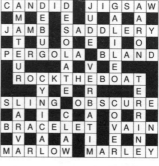

3

4

5

6

7

8

9

10

11

12

13

14

15

16

17

18

19

20

21

22

23

24

25

26

27

28

29

30

31

32

33

34

35

36

37

38

39

40

41

42

43

44

45

46

47

48

49

50

51

52

53

54

55

56

57

58

59

60

61

62

63

64

65

66

67

68

69

70

71

72

73

74

75

76

77

S	U	L	K		D	O	G	G	E	R	E	L
C		A			C		R		A		E	
A	R	M	Y		S	C	R	O	U	N	G	E
B		E		B		U		U		T		K
B	A	D	C	O	M	P	A	N	Y			
A		U		T		Y		D		J		C
R	E	C	I	T	E		S	L	E	A	Z	E
D		K		I		K		E		M		R
	A	C	C	E	S	S	I	B	L	E		
S		G		E		R		S		O		M
W	E	A	K	L	I	N	G		E	R	G	O
A		I		L		E			E		N	
T	A	N	G	I	B	L	E		D	E	N	Y

78

K	A	I	S	E	R		S	M	E	L	L	Y
	G		I		O		T		T		O	
F	R	E	T		S	Q	U	E	E	G	E	E
	O		A		E		B		R		S	
S	U	P	R	E	M	O		G	N	A	S	H
N			A		K		A					
	D	I	S	G	R	U	N	T	L	E	D	
			E		Y		I				R	
S	C	R	I	P		S	T	O	P	G	A	P
R		S		C		W		R			G	
P	E	R	M	E	A	T	E		I	D	O	L
	P		I		S		A		N		O	
R	E	S	C	U	E		R	O	T	U	N	D

79

|N|A|I|L| |A|D|J|U|T|A|N|T|
|A| |N| |S| |A| |N| |L| |A|
|V|I|T|A|L| |C|O|B|B|L|E|R|
|I| |H| |A| |T| |O| |I| |N|
G	R	E	A	T	L	Y		W	I	N	K	
A		S				L		E		G		E
T	R	A	N	C	E		O	D	I	O	U	S
E		M		U		U			O		O	P
	B	E	A	R		P	I	C	A	D	O	R
F		B		S		B		O		T		E
E	M	O	T	I	V	E		C	H	I	P	S
T		A		V		A		K		M		S
E	N	T	R	E	A	T	Y		P	E	T	O

80

M	U	T	E	S	W	A	N		N	U	T	S
A		E	T		N			T		N		O
I	C	E	B	E	R	G		O	T	T	E	R
M		T		A		O		B		R		O
	C	H	A	R		L	U	S	T	I	E	R
P			I		A			E			E	I
R	E	M	A	N	D		R	E	E	D	I	T
E		E			E		N					Y
S	A	T	C	H	E	L		S	T	I	R	
U		O		A		A		U		R		I
M	I	N	O	R		P	O	I	S	O	N	S
E		Y		T		S		T		N		I
D	E	M	O		R	E	L	E	A	S	E	S

NOTES